GROWTH AND REGULATION OF ANIMAL POPULATIONS

These Studies are designed to inform the mature student—the undergraduate upperclassman and the beginning graduate student—of the outstanding advances made in various areas of modern biology. The books will not be treatises but rather will briefly summarize significant information in a given field and interpret it in terms of our current knowledge of the rapidly expanding research findings within the life sciences. Also it is hoped that the Studies will be of interest to teachers and research workers.

BIOLOGY ←
STUDIES

Lawrence B. Slobodkin
University of Michigan
Ann Arbor

GROWTH AND REGULATION
OF ANIMAL POPULATIONS

Holt, Rinehart
and Winston
New York

▶
▶
▶
▶
▶ **to Dr. Abram Minkevitch**
▶
in accord with
Pirke Abot 6:3

JANUARY, 1962

COPYRIGHT © 1961 BY HOLT, RINEHART AND WINSTON, INC.
LIBRARY OF CONGRESS CATALOG CARD NUMBER: 61-7861
ALL RIGHTS RESERVED

27984-0111

PRINTED IN THE UNITED STATES OF AMERICA

preface ▶▶▶▶▶▶

The point of this book is to indicate briefly the present state of theory relating to the number and kinds of animals and plants that are found in nature. The subject is sufficiently new and the various attempts at constructing such a theory are so diverse that at present there is no convenient short, comprehensible term to designate this theory. "Ecology," the general term, is concerned with the inter-action between organisms and their environment in the broadest possible sense. Our problem here is somewhat more narrow and excludes, to a large degree, simple description of the natural world, on one hand, and much of the physiological reaction of individual organisms to their private worlds, on the other. We will be primarily concerned with interactions between individual animals that live in association with each other, insofar as these interactions in some way alter the number and kinds of these animals. Every reader will find some material in this book that appears trivially obvious to him. I doubt, however, that all of it will appear obvious to any one person or that any two readers will be in agreement as to which parts are obvious. Bear with me when I repeat, in a naive-sounding way, things you already know.

On occasion I will be forced to use algebraic notation. Every-thing stated in a mathematical form, however, will also be said verbally. If you have an allergy to notation, read only the prose and take my word for the rest.

By the end of the book I hope it will be clear that the problem of constructing a general theory of kind and abundance of animals is a real, empirically solvable problem; that we are not able to present a solution yet, but that the general procedures involved in such a solution are available at least in principle. I hope it will also be clear that this area represents an intellectual challenge of the first magnitude and that high-quality investigators are very much needed. The practical ramifications of this problem are as significant for the future survival of mankind as the solution to the problem of control of atom bombs.

The initial chapters describe in a general way the kinds of order and interaction that seem to exist in nature. We will then discuss some of the statistical properties that are used in the analysis of populations of individual species. With this background we will present experimental models of natural communities and some of the theory that has been constructed from them. Gradually we will generalize our experiments and theory until we return to the natural world, with perhaps a deeper comprehension than we had originally.

L. B. S.

Ann Arbor, Michigan
April, 1961

acknowledgments ▶▶▶

The National Science Foundation, the Rockefeller Foundation, and the Michigan Memorial Phoenix Project have at various times supported the research from my laboratory that is included in the text.

Francis Evans, Nelson Hairston, Fred Smith, and Marston Bates of the University of Michigan, Sumner Richman of Lawrence College, and Joseph Armstrong of Monteith College, Wayne State University, have all contributed criticism and encouragement.

On rereading, I find that the entire document is in one sense a commentary on some ideas of my teacher, G. Evelyn Hutchinson of Yale University.

The errors are my own.

contents

chapter one

Man in the
Ecological World

No matter how unique man may be from the standpoint of intellect, esthetics, or metaphysics, he has the same overall biological demands as any other animal. Despite the apparent complexity, self-sufficiency, and independence of human civilization, the laws governing population growth and maintenance in plants and animals are very similar to those governing population growth and maintenance in man. We will assume these statements to be axiomatic; the necessary qualifications and explanations will become apparent from the remainder of the text. The text will not be particularly concerned with man himself, except as one of many examples of a highly social population. To avoid interrupting the discussion later, it may be well to indicate initially man's role in nature and the practical significance of studies of nonhuman population dynamics.

Several authors (Brown, 1954; Darling, 1955; Elton, 1958; Osborn, 1948; Sears, 1935; Vogt, 1948) have discussed man's role in nature, and a recent impressive symposium volume (Thomas, 1956) discusses the effect of man on the earth. Without recounting the voluminous documentation in detail, certain conclusions may be drawn.

Civilization, particularly in its recent history, has been a major source of geologic change on the earth, equivalent in the magnitude of its effects to the natural geologic forces of rain and frost. The constructions arising from the efforts of man differ

1

from other features on the face of the earth in their relative lack of stability. Without the activity of man most of these changes would never appear at all, and without man's care and maintenance most of them would disappear. For example, metals typically exist on the earth's natural surface in an oxidized state. Man's metal structures, however, are made of reduced metals. The process of changing metals from the oxidized to the reduced state is one of the major power-consuming processes of civilization. Again, large masses of nonmetallic rock are typically acted upon by water, heat, and gravity to produce solid masses with sloping sides. Most of man's buildings are vertical walled and hollow. It is noteworthy that the few mound-shaped solid structures built by man have lasted longer than even the languages spoken by their architects. To make improbable objects and maintain them against dissolution requires tremendous expenditures of energy. Recently this energy has been supplied by the rapid dissolution, instigated by man, of otherwise relatively stable geologic formations, such as coal beds or subterranean oil pools.

Man's construction and maintenance act to alter the direction of some geologic changes and to increase greatly the rate of others. For most of its history the nonhuman biological world has existed under conditions of relatively slow geologic change, but the new geology of man—the geology of the noösphere—to use Vernadsky's term (1944), has brought about relatively rapid change in the lives of many organisms. Foxes, for example, have vanished from the rocks of Manhattan but rats have expanded into the tunnels and sewers.

In addition to altering the geologic surface of the earth, man acts directly on biological systems. He has eliminated some of the large organisms that he considered at the time to be dangerous or useless. The wolf has been eliminated from eastern North America and the lion from most of the Indian peninsula and the entire Middle East. Man does his futile best to eliminate some other species, which accounts for the drainage canals being dug in the New Jersey marshes, in which the mosquitoes continue to breed. Often a species or a population vanishes by accident because it happens to be in the way of some other biological effort of man. Various fish populations have died in man's feud with the mosquitoes. Bayberry, snails, cedars, large ungulates—all have had their populations decimated because they share a parasite with man or one of man's creatures.

Since man has food requirements similar to those of the other large mammals, he encourages the increase of certain plants and animals that provide him with food and with the peculiarly human requirements of clothing and ornament. In this process man, assuming the role of director of evolution, has appropriated at least 10 percent of the earth's surface.

Mountains, oceans, deserts, and even rivers act as barriers to many animals and some species of plants. Communities of mutually tolerant species have developed inside these barriers. Occasionally an animal is rafted or blown or harassed across a barrier and may momentarily upset the structure of nature on the new land. In such a case the new organism may replace some existing species or simply fit in with only a slight change in the abundance of the other species; most likely it will be unable to become established in the new location and will die.

In the course of his daily commerce man roams the earth, crossing these barriers, carrying—on his person or in the recesses of his ship, plane, canoe, or pocket—pets, pests, weeds, parasites, improvements and ornaments, both plant and animal. Dogs, cats, goats, and pigs have been spilled into every port-of-call. Fleas, rats, flies, ants, lice, and infinite varieties of microorganisms have stowed away on almost every journey man has ever made. Although rat guards on hawsers may do the work for which they were introduced, how does one prevent escape of beetles from an airplane? Under this hail of immigrants, radical changes are occurring in the nonhuman world wherever mankind passes.

Not only is man the most shocking innovation since the first appearance of the terrestrial vertebrates, but his activities are proceeding at an accelerating rate. Not only are the numbers of men on the earth increasing at almost 3 percent per year, but the standard of living of all men is rising, with a concomitant increase in the per capita demands for fuel and raw materials of all sorts. The importance of man continues to increase and the possibility of the biological world ever being as stable as it was in prehuman time becomes more and more remote. How many men can the earth hold? We must abandon all pretense of saving intact any wilderness areas and consider that we will treat the earth as a combined garden and factory; all other species will either prove useful to man or will be eliminated; they will either adjust to the omnipresence of man or die. Answers to the question are now merely guesses, ranging from 7 billion to 200 billion, the difference in the estimates depending on how several subsidiary questions are answered.

Implicit in this picture of the future is a mental health problem: a world completely full of man and his activities could well be a maddening place. There is an esthetic problem: the beauty of the wilderness is very real. There is a political problem: a world full of men would be highly regimented, a world of an Aldous Huxley or Orwell fantasy.

Even more terrifying is the eventual biological problem. Many of the elements on the surface of the earth are now being used and reused. The carbon in our atmosphere has passed through living things several times since the world began. The nitrogen in your breakfast may have been through four other organisms in the last four years. In general, plants bind the various elements that make up living stuff in an energy-rich form, using light energy from the sun in the process of photosynthesis. This energy is respired as fast as it is made. We know this, since organic compounds by and large do not accumulate anywhere, which would be the case if energy were not being respired. Plants respire only about a third of the photosynthetically fixed energy. Two-thirds goes into supplying the food for all the nongreen things that are alive on the earth. Since it is known that energy does not accumulate, and in most of America we can look out a window and see vegetation that shows no sign of being chewed or decimated by animals, we can infer that much of the energy is consumed by animals after it leaves the living plants. Bacteria and molds fill the soil and the microarthropods feed on them. The fact that the grasshoppers, caterpillars, and other organisms that feed directly on the live plants do not denude the leaves, except during unusual periods, indicates that something other than food shortage is controlling the numbers of these herbivores, the obvious inference being that they are controlled by predators. If the predators and decomposers are responsible for the lack of accumulation of organic material, then they must be limited in their abundance by the quantity of organic plant material available. In short, the absence of the accumulation of organic material implies that there exists a balance in nature in at least one sense. How far man can alter this nice balance without causing excess or defect in the rate of utilization of carbon dioxide in the atmosphere or the rate of silting of lakes and rivers, and what the effect would be on man of tripling the carbon dioxide concentration in the atmosphere, we do not know.

In addition to the gross cycles of water and carbon there are cycles of reuse occurring in the less conspicuous elements such as vanadium, cobalt, molybdenum, and barium. Quite often these hinge in a large part on the biological activities of a relatively few species. For example, sea squirts are of major significance in the passage of vanadium through the sea. How are these cycles affected by man and how may his present activities be altering them? Some of man's disturbances of nature are harmless, but it is quite possible that some of them may have ramifications that will seriously alter man's world. It is, unfortunately, impossible to determine, at the present time, the complete implications of any disturbance of nature. We can confidently say that as human populations and human standards of living and rates of per capita environment consumption increase, the margin for error in judgment diminishes.

The normal activities of man cannot continue without constant disruption of nature. The spread of population and railroads in India that has seriously interfered with the mating behavior of the Indian rhino (Ripley, 1952) is a case that generates only a certain amount of intellectual and perhaps sentimental regret. But are we as certain that various other results of our population growth will create only a diminution of the variability of nature? Some may be much more dangerous than that.

The primary problem is to ensure, so far as possible, that the disturbance produced by man is reversible. By keeping a careful check on what we may call "man-associated" nature it may be possible to see the effects of disturbance while we can still change our activities. Agricultural procedures have repeatedly been altered when it was found that soil conditions were deteriorating too rapidly. In some cases this has actually restored a semblance of *status quo ante*. If, as is quite likely, vital aspects of man's ecology are dependent on undomesticated species, nature sanctuaries not only are of esthetic, sentimental, and recreational value but are indispensable reserves of biological raw material to be used for the retracing of our ecological steps. Such retracing may become necessary for the construction of a viable ecology. It is impossible to reconstruct a particular species once it is extinct. Some species and communities of species have critical limits of perturbation, beyond which they cannot recover. These limits of resilience of the natural world are not now known in any particular case. All we know is that they do exist and that we must somehow determine what they are.

The natural world seems infinitely complex to the casual observer. We must admit this complexity as an empirical fact. Descriptions of nature can, then, be in one of two forms: we can describe it in all its complexity or we can analyze it into simpler parts and describe them. A direct description will be accurate only to the degree that it mirrors the complexity of the subject. It is no easier to make predictions from such a description than from casual observation itself. This does not denigrate the value of such description· Anyone who has worked in nature on a specific problem involving prediction is struck with the accuracy of the observations of some laymen. An example of this occurred while I was traveling to Sarasota, Florida, to take charge of the red tide investigation, and started talking to a fisherman on a bus between Daytona Beach and Melbourne. His conclusions about red tide, modified in some details, were essentially identical with the conclusions I published two years and $80,000 later. The fisherman, unfortunately, could not precisely define the evidence and arguments that led to his conclusions. He was therefore simply guessing correctly.

In problems with little risk involved, an educated guess is an acceptable guide to decision. As the penalties for error increase, however, it is vital that most of the intuitive portion of the guessing procedure be replaced by publicly verifiable theory. Although the red tide was an economically significant problem, it had no life-or-death ramifications, and so the fisherman's clever guess or my simple-minded theory were sufficient guides for recommendations. Unfortunately, ecological problems in the broad sense do become matters of life and death. Man is examining his own habitat and cannot afford to destroy it. We cannot expect public administrators to be trained naturalists and at the same time develop the necessary information about law and economics. Moreover, there is no clear evidence that anyone can think as nature does; some of our very best naturalists have made unfortunate errors when they built on this semimystical foundation. On the other hand, there is some evidence to indicate that the man who makes the dry theoretical analysis must have some personal experience of the natural world. Occasionally, population theories made by pure mathematicians, astronomers, and statisticians have proven sterile or dangerous, or both. There is good reason, also, to believe that without formal training the statements made by the lover of nature are nothing more than an ecstatic cry having esthetic meaning only.

Our only alternative is to attempt to analyze nature so that it may be described in a rigorous way and so that predictions can be derived by publicly repeatable procedures. Such a description of nature is fragmentary in the sense that all the population equations, community theory, and sampling statistics in the world will not appear identical with an actual landscape. A Chinese mountain landscape screen or the description in the Canticles of a spring morning are more similar to nature itself but unfortunately have less predictive value than the "unnatural"-looking equations. After pulling out of the natural world the various tangled threads that can be rigorously analyzed, we will examine them with some care and then try to put them back together and see how closely this synthetic mathematical fabric resembles the tapestry from which it was pulled. The two will probably not look very much alike, but we should then be able to define, to some degree, the difference between what we know on theoretical grounds and what we must yet do before we can build safe predictions.

It goes without saying that the predictions are required immediately, and the theories are still primitive and show every sign of growing slowly. This is an untenable situation for which I can offer no easy solution.

chapter two

Communities and Populations

If you were to make a fence around any region of the earth's surface and list the kinds and numbers of organisms found within that fence, you would be starting to define the problem of population ecology. Making an actual list and count of this type, however, is a painful operation for several reasons. The three most obvious will be listed.

First, it takes something of an expert to distinguish one kind of animal from another, and becoming an expert on some groups of animals may require years of study. There are, for example, 200,000 kinds of beetles and 50,000 kinds of protozoa. Two hundred different species of arthropods alone may be found in the soil under a 5-inch diameter circle.

Second, the actual numbers of organisms involved is very high in some cases. A half-million arthropods per square meter of soil, 10 million protozoa per liter of sea water, a billion bacteria per meter of mud—these would in many instances be common figures.

The third objection is that it is difficult to determine how reliable and meaningful any particular count may be. How many of the organisms in the area examined really belong there and how many are just passing through? If you examined the area tomorrow, would the animals and plants be the same in numbers and kinds as they are today? If the boundaries of your area were

8

shifted slightly, what would happen to the kinds and numbers of organisms in it? How far can any estimate be generalized?

Despite these problems there certainly does seem to be order in the natural world, and this order cries out for explanation. For example, a typical rural landscape, as seen from the side of a road, may include grassland or pasture land in the foreground, a row of bushes behind them, and in the distance a backdrop of trees. Another typical view might include a small pond, surrounded by marsh, with plowed land in the distance and a woodlot. It is obvious to the hunter that certain sorts of game will be found in forests rather than in the open fields, and it is clear that an angler will drop his hook in water rather than sand. Each of these intuitively recognized regions of the landscape may be called a "community."[1] The boundaries between the communities are usually readily recognizable by the boundaries between the most visible plants (referred to as dominant plants). Portions of the landscape can thus be catalogued in various ways. We can, for example, categorize on the basis of the geometric shape of the dominant vegetation—that is, grassland, forests, etc. Grassland is recognized by the arrangement of the dominant vegetation as a relatively low carpet of plants, each individual plant being relatively insignificant in size; forest, as a canopy of plants with most of the green portions at their tops, forming an open, shaded region around the stems or trunks of the individual plants. We normally think of grassland as something a man can look over the top of, and a forest as something a man walks through. Forests, grasslands, marshes, etc., can also be categorized in terms of the kinds of plants that form the dominant vegetation; an oak-hickory community, for example, is different from a spruce-hemlock forest community, and a buffalo-grass community is different from a dune-grass community.

Extensive field studies have made it possible, at least in parts of the United States, to map the location of different terrestrial communities, both by dominant vegetation type and general topography (Clements and Shelford, 1939) and by the associations of species, independent of topography (the biotic provinces of Dice).

---

[1] The term "community" is here used in a very broad sense, essentially identical with "ecosystem" as used by Dice (1952). The concept is more clearly defined on p. 11.

However, where a community covers a large area—for example, the Carolinian province, or the beech-maple community, in several states of the eastern United States—it is almost impossible to make detailed predictions about the flora or fauna of any subdivision of major ecological units, although it is generally possible to make some predictions about the kinds of organisms that will be present and the kind that will be absent. It is thus advisable to examine smaller regions of the earth's surface, which may prove more amenable to complete analysis. How are such areas to be chosen?

The eventual goal is to discover exactly what determines the numbers and kinds of organisms in each area. The area selected should therefore be one in which most or all of the various possible interactions between organisms, and between organisms and their environment, are comprehensible in local terms. A pond or small lake or even a relatively permanent puddle is more likely to meet these requirements than a field or forest of equal surface area or than the volume of water under an equal surface area in the ocean or one of the Great Lakes. There are two reasons for this. A pond or small lake is clearly differentiated from the surrounding countryside by a drastic change in physical properties, which in turn implies a sharp boundary in the distribution of most animals. Water and air are very different, and the kinds of organisms adapted to water are in general very different from the kinds of organisms adapted to air. Although a small oceanic area has the air-water interphase as its upper boundary, it is not bounded on the edges. Further, a pond or small lake is concave, which means that all passive organisms and their products will stay in the community and will leave the boundary of the pond only by active transport —either by their own movement, or by being carried by some other organism, or by some sudden flow of water. It is not surprising, therefore, that much of the modern theory of ecology has been developed in lakes and with aquatic organisms.

Even in the nonaquatic parts of nature, however, we want to be able to define subregions small enough to permit detailed analysis. Because of their tremendous size and complexity, whole forests and whole biotic provinces cannot be analyzed in detail. Enough work has been done in such areas to demonstrate the existence of regularities, but the more discrete and simple the systems studied, the more apparent these regularities become.

An assumption must then be made, namely, that the same ecological laws operate in a microcosm, such as a lake, as operate in a macrocosm, such as the Carolinian biotic province or the whole world.

Having made this assumption, we must determine whether lakes are the only microcosms we can deal with, or whether there are other more subtly defined small regions of the earth's surface in which most interactions occur within the area. The interactions we are concerned with may prove to be very elusive. One cold night or one hour of strong wind may make vast differences in the biological world. We cannot, in practice, wait in any area to watch interactions in general, particularly since we do not know a priori what kinds of interactions we are looking for; we only know, generally, that we are interested in all interactions that control or alter the number and kind of organisms found in a given region. If we then find two samples of earth surface that are identical in number and kind of organisms, we are justified in saying that the same kinds and intensities of interactions are occurring in the two areas. If the two samples were taken relatively close together and if there is reason to believe that samples taken in the intervening area would also be the same whereas samples taken in a surrounding area would be different, then the area of identical samples would be a microcosm in some sense. A spatially definable region of the earth that is characterized by the fact that a particular family of ecological interactions is occurring in it will be called a community. There are ambiguities in this concept as it has been stated, but the definition is sufficiently precise for the present if it permits us to delineate interesting study areas. As the nature of these interesting interactions becomes more explicit we will modify our definition of a community.

The interactions between organisms can take several forms:

(1) Altering the physical environment of another organism, as trees provide shade, or prairie dogs create holes, or earthworms change soil texture;

(2) Changing the chemical environment, as aquatic plants change the oxygen concentration of the water in a lake;

(3) Supplying some chemical compound, element, or energy

to another organism, as plants supply energy when eaten or as rabbits supply amino acids to wolves.

These interactions may be direct, as in the few examples cited above, or indirect. We can imagine, for example, that wolves can interact with coyotes by simply increasing the rate of energy transfer from rabbits to wolves.

All communities are open in the sense that there must be an inflow of either radiant energy or chemically bound energy. All communities must be in a steady state or close to a steady state in that the outflow of energy, either as heat or as chemically bound energy, must approximate the inflow. If the communities are to be in a chemical steady state, the same equality of outflow and inflow must apply to all chemical elements. The concept of "close to a steady state" can be explained as follows. An examination of a community either will show great changes to have taken place from the time of initiation of the study to the time of its termination, as in the preclimax community of a hay infusion (Woodruff, 1912), or will show it to be essentially the same community at the beginning and the end of the study, as in the old field successions in Michigan (Evans and Cain, 1952). The community in the second case may be considered as being close to a steady state, since the net changes occurring during the course of the study are probably smaller than the sampling error involved in their estimation.

It will be noted that our definition of community is sufficiently broad to permit an area of almost any size to be used as an object of study, ranging from the earth as a whole to an experimental population container. Certain aspects of the interaction between organisms can be determined by studying the organisms themselves; other aspects, by studying the processes that organisms affect. We will be primarily concerned with relatively simple systems that are capable of fairly detailed analysis. The assumption here is that the more complex systems are actually assemblies of simpler systems even though the simplicity of their components cannot be readily demonstrated in the field. The simplest systems, from the analytic standpoint, are either the very big ones, like the distribution of carbon in the entire biosphere (that is, in the biologically inhabited portion of the earth's surface, including both the atmosphere and oceans and sediments of biological origin) or the distribution and dynamics of plankton in the Atlantic ocean, or the very small ones, like the growth of populations of bacteria or yeast in laboratory test tubes. The difficult middle ground of the visible landscape can be rigorously dealt with only by inference. Certain difficulties are inherent in both the very big and the very small systems: the former are inaccessible to experimentation and the latter are unnatural. Nevertheless, it is possible to ask specific questions about real communities that can be answered experimentally and theoretically, and certainly all the conclusions of the experimentalists and theoreticians must eventually be formulated in such a way as to permit a field test.

Many field studies have demonstrated the fact that even on a very local scale the distribution of organisms on the earth is far from random. Once we demonstrate a lack of randomness, we demonstrate the existence of orderly, natural laws that should be able to predict observed ecological patterns, even though we may not, at the moment, know how to formulate these laws. Hairston and Byers (1954), to choose one actual example out of the many in the literature, report on the distribution of soil arthropods in an abandoned field in Michigan. In terms of dominant vegetation, the field is a grasslands community surrounded by a deciduous forest. The question was to determine whether the border of trees coincided with the borders of a microcosm that was in any sense self-contained or whether there was some other subtly defined border within the field itself. Thirty-five samples of soil were removed from the field and the microarthropods extracted, identified, and counted. The samples were chosen to avoid any obvious relation with the forest; for example, no samples were taken directly under the two hickory trees that stood in the field. One hundred seventy-seven species of microarthropods were found in the 35 samples; 138 species were found in 13 or fewer of the samples. Fourteen species were found in from 14 to 24 of the samples, and the 25 most frequently occurring species were found in between 25 and 35 of the samples. That is, many species occurred in only a few of the 35 samples, but 25 species were found in almost all of the samples. Using these 25 most frequently occurring species as indicating in some sense the typical association of species for the field, Hairston and Byers then drew a line on a map of the field separating those sample locations in which 21 or more of the 25 most common species occurred from those sample locations in which 20 or fewer of the 25 most common species occurred. It was found that the samples that did not have at least 21 of the 25 most common species present in the field were all located along the eastern and southern edge of the field and extended toward the center of the field only in the regions associated with the two hickory trees. In short, there was an ecological difference, invisible on gross inspection, between the northwestern and central portions of the field and the southern and eastern portions. Also, the two isolated hickory trees seemed to extend the boundaries of the forest into the field. The center of the field was effectively homogeneous ecologically. Hairston further found that whereas there was a clear distinction between the soil arthropods of the open field and those influenced by the forest border and the hickory trees, even within the open fields the arthropod fauna in the bottom of the shallow swales was different from that on the low ridges or uplands between the swales. The total surface relief of the field did not exceed ten feet. In this case there was a definite vegetation difference between the swale bottoms and the ridge tops, with slightly more luxuriant vegetation in the damper swales than on the more rapidly drained ridges. On the same field Evans and Dahl (1956) have shown that the distribution of plant species was largely determined by variations in moisture content, soil stability, and shade.

Engelman (1960), sampling the same locations seven years later, found the upland distribution of mites, which are the major soil arthropod group, to be very different from that reported by Hairston and Byers. This was not simply a difference between investigators, since Hairston made new collections and confirmed the results of Engelman. Evans and Cain (1952) had already shown that this field was undergoing a gradual return to forest after having been plowed land between approximately 1870 and 1900 and having served as a pasture until 1928. A herd of white-tailed deer still feed on the field and in the surrounding woodland.

Engelman believes that the difference in the mite fauna that became apparent in the seven-year period between his work and that of Hairston is due to a radical alteration in the fungal and possibly bacterial flora of the field. Certainly the change of the higher plants in the field, indicated by Evans and Cain, is very minor for a seven-year period. If this suspected change in fungal population is confirmed it will be an excellent example of very inconspicuous changes in plants producing relatively drastic changes in animal distribution and abundance.

The same type of ecological differentiation within a homogeneous-looking region can also be found among plant communities. There are many methods of analyzing plant communities, but only a particularly interesting recent study will be cited here. Williams and Lambert (1959) analyzed two areas in England, one with five species of vascular plants in significant numbers and one with ten. The five-species community was sampled by taking a rectangular grid of samples at five-meter intervals—615 samples on a 44 by 14 grid in which each sample consisted of a one-meter quadrat (one sample was lost). Since any one of the five species could be either present or absent from any one sample, there are 32 possible types of samples (2^5). Only twelve of these were actually found. The investigators subdivided the samples into classes, so that within each group of samples the co-occurrence of any two species is not significantly different from the co-occurrence expected by chance alone. The details of this procedure are not necessary to our present argument, but an abbreviated discussion of the procedure is presented using the five-species case as an example.

Let N equal the number of samples. Let A, B, C, D, and E equal the number of samples in which at least one individual of species A, B, C, D, and E respectively occur. By chance, the proportion of samples in which both species A and species B occur would be expected to be AB/N^2 and the number of such samples is $AB/N^2 \times N = AB/N = E_{AB}$.

Let the observed number of samples in which both A and B occur equal O_{AB}. The probability that O_{AB} differs from E_{AB} by chance alone can be determined by computing

$$\chi^2 = \frac{[(E_{AB} - O_{AB}) - 1]^2}{E_{AB}} \text{ [2]}$$

The smaller the value of χ^2, the greater the probability that

[2] The subtraction of 1 from the absolute value of $E_{AB} - O_{AB}$ is Yates' correction for continuity. Chi square is taken with one degree of freedom. See the original paper for discussion of the rationale of this procedure.

O_{AB} and E_{AB} differ only by chance. If the calculated value exceeds 3.481, this probability is less than 5 percent. The implication would then be that something other than random variation is causing species A to occur in the same samples as species B if the sign of $E_{AB} - O_{AB}$ is negative, or not to occur in the same samples as B if the sign of the difference between expected and observed is positive.

Williams and Lambert construct a table (Table 2-1) in which are entered all significant values of χ^2 for the association between pairs of species—that is, all values of χ^2 greater than 3.841.

Table 2-1

Significant Values of χ^2 for Association between Pairs of Species (italicized values indicate negative association) (From Williams and Lambert, 1959)

	A	B	C	D	E
A	. .	51.31	45.66	x	x
B	51.31	. .	93.76	*12.62*	*68.64*
C	45.66	93.76	. .	*4.84*	*14.08*
D	x	*12.62*	*4.84*	. .	6.92
E	x	*68.64*	*14.08*	6.92	. .
Total	96.97	226.33	158.34	24.38	89.64

The chi-square values are then summed, regardless of sign for each species. It is clear from the table that no species is randomly distributed with regard to all four of the other species in the field, although species A is randomly distributed with reference to both D and E. Species D and E seem to avoid association with B and C. The greatest departure from random distribution is found in species B. In other words, the field shows the greatest heterogeneity from the standpoint of species B. By dividing the samples into two groups, one with B present and the other with B absent, we should obtain relatively homogeneous groups of samples. Two new tables of χ^2 are now constructed.

The only significant association in Table 2-2 is between A and C, and in Table 2-3 between A and D, showing that A and C are tied in the presence of B whereas A and D are tied in the absence of B. Reference to Table 2-1 shows that the sum of χ^2 for C is greater

Table 2-2

Significant Values of χ^2 for Samples in Which B Is Present

	A	C	D	E
A	. .	24.8	x	x
C	24.8	. .	x	x
D	x	x	. .	x
E	x	x	x	. .

Table 2-3

Significant Values of χ^2 for Samples in Which B Is Absent

	A	C	D	E
A	. .	x	4.34	x
C	x	. .	x	x
D	4.34	x	. .	x
E	x	x	x	. .

than that for A, which in turn is greater than that for D. This information is used to make the next division on the basis of presence or absence of C when B is present and on the presence or absence of A when B is absent. The samples have now been divided into four groups with no association at all existing within each group.

Slight alterations in statistical procedure, or in the choice criterion where there are ties, will alter the final categorization slightly in this case, but in any case four groups with no association within groups would result and the distribution of the groups on the original field will be much the same.

When the various classes are plotted on the map of the original field, it is found that they do form a reasonable, if nonobvious, pattern: the major ecological division in the field corresponded to the location of the edge of the geologic formation known as the Plateau Gravel Ridge. The edge of the gravel was a less conspicuous feature to the observers than was the sign of an old burn that had covered a portion of the field. In this case, at least, the complex statistical procedure was more than just a difficult way of stating the obvious.

A similar analysis in the ten-species community demonstrated a somewhat more complex pattern in which it was possible to determine the outlines of a zone of burning six years old under a zone of burning two years old. The plant associations were clearly distinct, although the superficial topography and appearance of the field were relatively homogeneous.

On the basis of elementary physiological information and the known heterogeneity of the inanimate landscape, we might have expected that species are not randomly distributed, even on a very local scale. It is of some importance, then, to interpret the existence of small areas in which association between species is actually random. The randomness of this association does not necessarily imply that the individuals of each species are themselves randomly distributed. (Note that we have been using presence or absence as our criterion and not number or mass of individuals.) What is implied is that from the standpoint of the species concerned, those areas over which the random distribution occurs are identical. A different group of species would not necessarily have the same criteria of identity, nor need there be any biological cause for the identity between areas. If, however, we are concerned with defining some ultimate unit of homogeneity for natural associations of species, it is eminently reasonable to consider as such a unit an area in which the association between species is random; and the work of Williams and Lambert is of great value in demonstrating that such units do exist and can actually be found in nature by an objective procedure.

Those species that are randomly associated with each other in a single field may actually have very strong interactions either with each other or with some climatic or geological feature of the environment that is itself occurring on the *entire* field. Associations between two species would then become apparent only on a larger scale of sampling. This is equivalent to stating that no two species, with the possible exception of a parasite and its host, have identical geographical distributions.

On a sufficiently large scale, all species exhibit clumping. As the scale of observation becomes smaller, however, the clumping becomes less and less pronounced and finally becomes either infradispersion or randomness (Fig. 2-1).

An infradispersed species is one in which the individuals tend

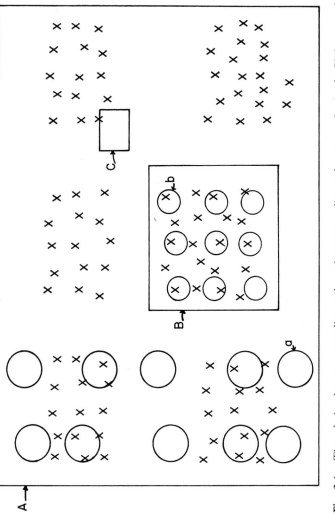

Fig. 2-1. The relation between sampling scale and apparent dispersal pattern of animals. If the area of interest is *A* and the samples are the large circles *a*, then the organisms (*X*) appear clumped. If the area of interest is *B* and the samples are the small circles *b*, then the organisms (*X*) appear infradispersed. If the area of interest is *C*, then the organisms appear extremely rare.

to maintain a more or less constant distance to their nearest neighbor. This is particularly noticeable among organisms that compete very strongly with each other. Dune plants, for example, are spaced regularly because of competition for water; male birds are regularly spaced because of the phenomenon of territoriality, where each bird maintains possession of a piece of land and makes it impossible for any other male to settle in it. A random distribution of animals in space is a relatively rare phenomenon, found primarily in situations where the position of the individual organism is dependent almost completely on air or water movements with a high turbulence. Another explanation for what may appear as random dispersion by turbulence is to consider the entire area to be equivalent from the standpoint of the organism for some biological reason. It would then be implied that the population is such a highly integrated system that its influence on each individual is constant, regardless of the individual's position.

The ultimate subgroups, in which the species are distributed at random with respect to each other, constitute some sort of final level of ecological homogeneity. The samples in these final groupings are representatives of spatial areas that are identical, at least from the standpoint of the species present.

We have demonstrated that definite organization, as well as definite spatial heterogeneity, exists in nature and that, at least in two English fields and, by inference, in a wide variety of other regions, there are small spatial areas that differ from each other so slightly as to be effectively identical from the standpoint of the species involved. We could define these small spatial areas as communities, but we will see later that the concept of community is more interesting if it is defined in terms of chemical and energetic transfer between organisms. For the present we can think of a community in a common-sense way as any readily definable group of organisms, together with the physical world that houses them, that can be conveniently studied and may be expected to show interesting interactions.

An analogy with human sociology would perhaps clarify this definition. A public highway or a strip town along a highway is a poor study region for the sociologist, since many of the factors that determine the role of the persons he is likely to encounter are dependent on things that are outside his study area. More interesting results are likely to be found in communities that are partially or completely isolated from outside influences. The degree of outside influence is easier to assess in human populations than it is in ecological communities.

The fascination of a lake or its obverse, an island, for an ecologist lies largely in the fact that there is a minimum of transfer of organisms between this area and the larger communities that surround it. All of the laws that control number, kind, and interaction between organisms must therefore have their full operation within the limits of such an area. This is an almost perfect community—that is, one in which all energetic and chemical transfer, with the exception of light energy from the sun and heat energy from respiration, is found and expended within the community. A completely balanced aquarium would be a perfect community. (Note that no one has yet produced a sealed balanced aquarium.)

Does the existence of distributional homogeneity of plants and animals in certain areas imply that these are perfect communities? Not necessarily. Note, for example, that in the field studied by Hairston and Byers the main producers of chemically bound useful energy were the grasses, lichens, and mosses at the surface of the ground. These, in turn, fed the fungi that apparently were the main source of food for the microarthropods in the soil (Engelman, 1960). There was no known discontinuity of grass species distribution to correspond to the observed discontinuities in microarthropod distribution found in the field. The central field community, therefore, shared its producer species with the field-edge community. At the outer border of the field, a more complete transition was made in all plant species; whether this transition affected the animal species is not now known, but it probably did. Without a sharp physical discontinuity it is very difficult to establish the boundaries of a community; hence the key term in the definition of community is probably "conveniently studied." It is obvious that more is likely to be learned from certain areas than from others and that underlying relations between organisms may be obscured by inept choice of study area.

Although it seems clear that the distribution and abundance of organisms are at least partially dependent on interaction between the organisms themselves, the notion has been seriously advanced that the inanimate world is the sole control on communities. The ideal refutation of this concept would be a demonstration that the addition or deletion of one species from a community can radically and permanently alter the relative abundance and even the species composition of the remainder of the community. (The long-term basis must be mentioned so as to exclude the meaningless device of removing the plants from a community and then watching the animals starve to death.)

In turning attention from the general landscape to a single species, several questions arise. What determines the gross distribution of a species on the earth's surface? What determines its local distribution? What controls the numbers of animals of a particular species in each location? The last of these will be of chief concern in a later discussion, but the others will be briefly taken up here.

There is an element of historical accident in the geographic distribution of each species. The rapid transport devices of men have lessened the importance of this element recently, particularly for small and inconspicuous forms, but it is still notable, as indicated by the spread of very recent invaders in various parts of the world. Fire ants, armadillos, and opossums seem to be changing their present distribution in the United States much more rapidly than would be expected on the basis of observed climatic change, and the indications are that the suitable environments for these species are in no sense limited to those in which they are presently found. Species adapted to a particular area may be absent from that area simply by historical accident. Either the properties of the area were different when the species was in contact with it, or the species evolved in some similar area without any connection with the area in question.

As a rule, however, an organism that is moved from an area in which it is normally found to one in which it is not normally found simply dies, either because of inability to withstand the new climate or to adapt to new food species or to avoid new predators, or because suitable cover is unavailable. Occasionally an individual organism may survive but fail to produce a population, an example being the camels released in New Mexico by the United States Army. The reason for not starting a population, given initial survival, is often lack of a mate or lack of appropriate opportunities for social interactions. On occasion a sufficient level of crowding may be a prerequisite for population survival. It has become unlikely for two rhinoceroses of opposite sex to meet and breed on the Indian subcontinent since they are very rare and the male's period of sexual activity is very short (Ripley and Hutchinson, 1954). Many other cases, in which interactions between organisms of the same species result in improved survival or reproduction, are listed by Allee (1951).

The suitability of a given region for a particular species can sometimes be determined on the basis of measurements of one or more environmental variables. "Climatographs" have been used in this way to indicate areas suitable for insects (Bodenheimer, 1958). A climatograph consists of a two-dimensional graph in which the ordinate represents mean temperature (usually monthly) and the abscissa represents rainfall. On the surface so defined, the values for a particular region of these factors are plotted. If it can be established that some species found in that region is capable of rapid increase during one portion of the year and if it is further found that that species occurs only in regions where there is a similar set of temperatures and rainfall, then the ecological "niche" of the species in question has been defined—at least with regard to temperature and rainfall. We will return to the concept of the ecological niche later.

The few available cases that show the distribution of one species to be clearly limited by the presence of another indicate that part of the observed orderliness in nature is of biological origin rather than simply a climatic effect. This can be strongly demonstrated by upsetting certain aspects of the biological orderliness. Specifically, in some cases where man has spilled species into areas in which they do not normally occur, these species have become extremely common or have become pests. Pests, in this sense, are defined as species that make it difficult for man or one or more of man's associates to survive and flourish. It seems apparent, from the cases of transport of species summarized by Elton (1958), that the more complex a community, in the sense of having a greater number of species and a greater number of interactions between species, the smaller the likelihood that an invader can become established; or, if it becomes established, the smaller the likelihood of its becoming a pest.

The establishment of an invader implies either that the ecological role (or niche) appropriate to the invader was unoccupied in the invaded community, or that there had been no natural selection to enforce the most efficient exploitation of the niche by its original occupant. Either condition is less likely in a complex community than in a simple one. The likelihood that an invader will be considered a pest increases if it concentrates its ecological effect on one or a few species rather than exerting a small effect on a wide variety of species, and this, again, is more likely in a simple than in a complex community. The simplification of the natural world caused by the transformation of wild land into arable seems to encourage the onslaughts of pests and invaders, for agricultural land is normally occupied by very few species and is extremely simple.

Cases in which it can definitely be demonstrated that the distribution of one species is limited by that of another are relatively rare. This is because we can examine only the present landscape, which is the stable end result of the relatively rapid interactions between species.

chapter three

The Ecological Niche in a General Sense

We established, by implication, in our initial discussion of communities that the distribution of any one species on the earth's surface is not random, either with respect to other species or with respect to the physical parameters of the environment. We also referred to the concept that each species has a role or a "job" in nature, usually termed a "niche." In this niche the species is capable of maintaining itself in an approximate steady state. It may be either common or rare in its niche—and we will discuss this below—but in any case it is persistent. The climatograph of the areas in which the species is actually found represents in a general sense the temperature-rainfall parameters of the ecological niche. There are other parameters that are also significant, at least in principle.

Hutchinson (1957) has presented a formal analysis of this concept. The upper and lower limits of a set of environmental variables X_i, that will permit maintenance of a steady-state population of a particular species, S, will be designated as X'_i and X''_i respectively. Consider any two such variables, X_1 and X_2, to be plotted on a set of rectangular coordinates. If X_1 and X_2 are independent and if the maintenance of a steady-state population is an all-or-none event, then we can define a rectangular area, each point of which corresponds to a pair of values of X_1, X_2 that would permit the species S_1 to survive. Adding a third variable would correspondingly produce a volume, and similarly, the variables

$X_4, \cdots, X_n$ can be introduced, producing an n-dimensional hypervolume, every point of which corresponds to an environmental state that will permit S_1 to survive. This hypervolume is referred to by Hutchinson as N_1—the "fundamental niche" of S_1.

Consider a volume of ordinary space, B. It may contain a variety of subregions, more or less separate from each other, in which all of the values, $X_1, X_2, \cdots, X_n$, are such that these subregions correspond to part of the hypervolume N_1. If we define the class of all hypervolumes $N_1, N_2, \cdots$ as N, then, in general, any sufficiently large volume on the earth is likely to contain points corresponding to one or more of the points in one or more fundamental niches of N; in other words, it is quite likely that at least some organisms will be found in any sufficiently large sample of space. It is also clear that since B is limited in volume, it need not contain any points that correspond to any of the points of any particular N_1 in N, or, as stated by Hutchinson, B may be incomplete with respect to N_1. This is another way of saying that not all species are physiologically capable of maintaining their steady state in any given volume of space.

Although this analysis permits an unequivocal statement of what we would like to mean by ecological niche, it has several practical difficulties.

For one thing, it is most likely that the probability of steady-state maintenance must be considered at each point in N_i rather than the all-or-none definition we have made. Moreover, for many environmental variables, linear ordering is not possible. Configurational properties of various sorts must be considered. For example, it is known that light intensity is of primary significance in determining the outcome of competition between brown and green species of hydra. It seems likely, however, that not only the mean light intensity but the pattern of incident radiation is significant. It may be expected that a dish half covered with black paper, and therefore having only half the incident light of an uncovered dish, will be effectively as well lit to a green hydra as an uncovered dish, but not as well lit as a dish with a gray cover. The pattern of striping or patterning on the surface of the dish may prove significant, but it is not conveniently linearly ordered.

Hutchinson is concerned over the fact that in this scheme, diurnal and nocturnal species are in separate niches, although they may compete for food, space, etc. This purely conceptual difficulty is overcome if we consider that certain of the parameters used to define a niche will themselves have a temporal extension while others will not. To the degree that two species compete for some property of their environment that has temporal extension they can compete without ever meeting face to face. Expendable resources, particularly those involving energy in some form, like the rate of energy fixation by photosynthesis in the community or the rate at which energy is made available in some other form to the community, may limit the growth of the several species in a community. The energy in a bit of food, once eaten, cannot be reused. Food eaten in the morning is unavailable in the evening; hence a population active in the morning (that of an insectivorous bird, for example) will have a competitive effect on an insectivorous population active in the evening (that of a small species of bat, for example), even though the two populations may never meet. Space, on the other hand, is a classic case of a time-free variable. Two populations can compete for space only if they simultaneously utilize the space. The time relations involved in competitive interaction are of primary significance, as will be seen when we discuss scavenger-host relations.

We will be discussing populations in either actual or theoretical discrete containers or volumes. Hutchinson's concept of the niche is particularly significant for our purpose, in that it permits unequivocal statement of the fact that any actual physical space in which a population of animals is living is a subregion of the more broadly defined fundamental niche peculiar to the species. It may be further expected that the physiological properties of even a single species will be variable over the range of conditions presented by its fundamental niche.

We have defined the concept of an ecological niche by considering a hypervolume defined by parameters within which a population of a species in question could maintain a steady state. Within an ecological niche, considered as a spatial unit, the critical interactions are those between members of the same species. Before we can develop a theory of natural communities we must know the various properties of a single species in a single ecological niche.

To the casual observer, the most obvious ecological properties of particular species are commonness and rareness. These may be manifested in terms of presence or absence of a species from fairly large regions. For example, the rarity of elephants in Iowa is extreme, and although Ann Arbor, Michigan, is in the range of the snowy owl it is quite obvious that snowy owls are much rarer than fox squirrels. Ann Arbor is also in the range of flying squirrels, but although flying squirrels are more common than snowy owls, they are not usually apparent to the casual observer because of their nocturnal habits.

To a large extent commonness and rareness of species are controlled by exogenous factors such as temperature, humidity, or the presence of appropriate foods or quantity of available food. Occasionally more subtle exogenous controls affect commonness or rareness; for example, certain club-mosses are limited by the concentration of aluminum in the soil, and certain of the empid flies are limited to single species of cedar trees. Bizarre limitations sometimes occur: there are various species of fish that live either among the tentacles of otherwise poisonous organisms like the Portuguese man-of-war or even, in one case, in the cloaca of certain sea cucumbers.

Occasionally, commonness and rareness are controlled by peculiarities of the species themselves. For example, the common spring beauty, when it occurs at all in a wooded region, will form a pinkish carpet over the surface of the ground, but showy lady's-slipper will be spaced in at least 20-foot intervals. Grasshoppers in a field or lawn are more or less randomly distributed, but ants will distribute their nests so as to make in general a maximum distance between nests of ants of the same species. Of course, the territorial behavior of birds and of many of the mammals and some of the reptiles and amphibians also is a factor controlling commonness and rareness in any particular local spatial region.

A population of any particular species can be characterized by its presence or absence in any given region or by its rareness and commonness in those regions where it is present. Presence and commonness also vary temporally; for example, the world over, after a heavy rain small boys find earthworms on sidewalks. Sometimes there is a local temporal variation; on the west coast of Florida, for example, a heavy rain is followed approximately ten days later by heavy adult mosquito populations.

In temperate regions, the overwhelming source of temporal

variations is the annual cycle of seasons with the accompanying temperature, sunlight, and rainfall fluctuations. In fact, if any species is found to vary in its abundance on an annual basis, it can safely be assumed that its abundance is keyed to one of the factors that vary with the astronomical year.

Changes in commonness or rareness on time scales longer than an annual cycle may be due to a variety of factors. Many of these variations are noncyclic; that is, they are gross environmental changes that lead to extinction of one or more species. In recent times extinction has almost invariably been associated with some consequence of man's activity.

The numbers of any particular species at any particular place commonly fluctuate on a finer time scale and in some particular circumstances may fluctuate over a longer than annual period. Nevertheless, if a sufficiently long time period is examined it is found that the mean number of animals in any particular species or in any particular region is constant. We can therefore assume that the ecological world is in a steady state.

At this point it is advisable to expand the notion of biological steady state. The term "biological steady state" is used on three different levels that differ in subject matter referred to and in time scale. A single organism is always changing in time. It is either growing fatter or growing thinner, reproducing or recovering from reproduction, or simply growing older. There is some evidence that if other factors are kept equal, time itself makes no difference in the physiology of some organisms. These potentially immortal organisms may include some flatworms (Armstrong, 1960) and some of the coelenterates. Sir D'Arcy Thompson (1940) reports a sea anemone named Granny that was kept in an aquarium for 60 years. During this time no changes whatsoever were apparent in the physiology of the animal. For most organisms, however, the concept of steady state on an individual basis is meaningless for time scales in excess of one-tenth the mean life expectancy of the animal.

At the other extreme, if we deal with times of the order of millions of years it will be found that new species may have arisen and some species disappeared, but that in general the total quantity of animal tissue and the total mass of plants on the surface of the earth have remained essentially constant—as has the chemical composition of the earth's crust, the salt concentration of the ocean, and the gas composition of the atmosphere.

If we consider a time scale of the order of halves of billions of years, however, it might be expected that the slow chemical changes occurring in the earth's surface will be of sufficient magnitude to disrupt the evolutionary steady-state condition.

The studies of Kurten (1959) indicate that ecological steady states will be disrupted by evolutionary changes during time intervals of the order of one-half million years. Intervals of this order may be termed "evolutionary time." At the other extreme, excessively short periods of observation may produce misleading estimations of steady-state conditions on the basis of minor perturbations in either the animals or their environment. Such short time intervals may be termed "physiological time." On the scale of ecological time—that is, over intervals of the order of ten times the length of one generation—populations may be expected to maintain an approximately steady state.

On an absolute time basis, steady-state conditions for individual bacteria can be measured in periods of minutes. It may take 24 or 48 hours before the physiological steady-state condition is violated in men, elephants, buffalo, tortoises, or most of the other large animals. Corresponding population steady states involve times of the order of days or weeks for bacteria, months for water fleas, and centuries or conceivably tens of centuries for man. Henceforth, we will be dealing with time scales of the order of ten times the generation time of the species involved—that is, ecological time.

On this time scale it is possible to set up a generalized series of differential equations to express the mutual interdependence of the organisms and their dependence on the nonliving world. On the simplest level the variables in such a set of equations need represent only extremely coarse categories of the world. For example, it is possible to discuss steady-state distribution of water in the earth's outer shell and atmosphere without making any particular distinction between the kinds of terrestrial plants or the kinds of terrestrial animals. If the steady-state distribution of energy in the biosphere is being discussed, the interesting entities are the sun, green plants, nongreen plants (including bacteria), herbivores, and the higher orders of carnivores.

Similar sets of equations could be made for any chemical element or for any chemical or physical entity for which an existence criterion of an operational sort can be stated. Some of these systems—for example, the steady-state distribution of heat in biological organisms—are not particularly interesting biologically. Others, like potential energy, or water, or any of the elements, are of very great interest.

The variable that will be chosen in the equation system will vary from entity to entity. The only basic requirement is that the sum of changes of any given entity across any given boundary in the world must be zero. The generalized equations for ecological steady states are most explicitly stated by Lotka (1956) as:

$$\frac{dX_i}{dt} = F_i(X_1, X_2, \cdots, X_n; P, Q, \cdots)$$

which simply states, "in any ecological system a change in any quantity X_i is dependent upon a set of quantities X_1, X_2, X_n, and a series of parameters P, Q, etc." If dX_i/dt is not equal to zero, evolution is taking place. In ecological time, evolution can be ignored or, when necessary, assumed to be absent. It is completely impractical to determine all of the values that would be required to make actual use of Lotka's generalized steady-state equation system.

We will now temporarily abandon the complexity of the natural world and attempt to construct experimental and theoretical models of simplified situations. When these have been understood it may be possible to return to an examination of nature with a better comprehension of the problems that confront us.

Because of the vast number of different species of animals, a careful analysis of the complete field of animal interaction may be subjected to enormous difficulties a priori. In fact, it may seem a hopeless task. For example, imagine that theoretical physics, instead of having the 20 or 30 elementary particles it now has, had the approximately 800,000 particles that might represent the species of known beetles. Were a man to succeed in very carefully and completely describing the population dynamics of one species of beetle, he would have done only 1.25×10^{-4} of the work required to describe the population dynamics in all the species of beetles, let alone the work needed to determine interactions between species of beetles. Fortunately, certain conclusions can be derived that are generally applicable to animal populations both in the field and in the laboratory.

For example, it will be demonstrated that all populations, at least in principle, can come to a steady state. For all populations a steady state has certain common characteristics; in particular, the rate of inflow of energy and the rate of expenditure of energy are equal and constant in mean value. Further, the mean age composition of the population over time is constant, as is the physiological history of any animal born into the population. The initial step in this study will be to analyze as carefully as possible the properties of such steady states in animal populations and communities.

In addition to the steady state there is another characteristic state that a population can attain and that will be similar from species to species. If a small number of organisms are introduced into an extremely large environment, they will tend to increase according to the "Malthusian" increase rate. If this increase continues for a sufficiently long period of time, characteristic structural properties of the population become apparent; such properties as age distribution, reproductive rate, and physiological history again approach constant values. We will analyze the properties of a population growing at a "Malthusian" rate of increase.

No population can continue to grow indefinitely at an exponential rate. In fact, there must be a transition between the logarithmic growth and the steady state when the environment is saturated with animals. This transition, while differing between species, has certain generalizable properties. Discussion of these populations will lead us to certain theorems relating to the type of specific physiological differences—for example, age and size—that do occur between individuals of single species.

After a brief analysis of the transition between logarithmic and steady-state population conditions, we will be able to examine in fair detail the thermodynamic efficiency of at least one population in producing protoplasm from food.

Finally, it will be found that behavior and social structure, in the sense used by the group psychologist or the animal behaviorist, is of definite evolutionary and ecological significance in the growth and maintenance of populations.

chapter four ▸ Life Insurance

for Animals

One of the first questions that may be asked about a population of animals is, "How long do they live?" The most facile answer is, "It depends," which is not at all satisfactory. The question of how long an animal lives is really a combination of several questions. It may mean the greatest age that can be attained by an animal of the species. Hediger (1950), reporting the length of time various zoo animals have been kept in captivity, finds 50 years for a male condor, 55 years for a "giant salamander," 30 years for bears, and 20 years for lions and other big cats. Flower has attempted to trace the authenticity of various accounts of extreme age in captive animals. He finds that some of these records admit of the possibility that a particularly beloved animal in a public menagerie may be replaced by an animal that is given the same name, and the age at death of the substitute is given as the combined age of the original animal and the "ringer" (Flower, 1947). Jumbo's female companion "Princess Alice" was reported to have died in Australia in 1941, which would make her age 157 years; the catch is that sometime during her life she seems to have changed species, being born as an African elephant and dying as an Asiatic elephant. Jumbo himself has had several ringers of this sort. More reliable estimates of elephants' age give a maximum of 67 years for Indian elephants and slightly less for African elephants. Two female tortoises (*Testudo graeca*) named Panhard and Daimler

33

were alive and still growing at the end of 39 years (Flower, 1944). Hediger reports "vultures" living "over a hundred years," a finding presumably based on a Griffon vulture formerly in the private menagerie of Prince Eugène, Duc de Savoye, which passed to a public menagerie after the owner's death and is reported to have lived 117 years. Public relations and nationalistic fervor make this record questionable (Flower, 1938).

Age estimates of animals in nature are generally derived from less direct evidence and will be discussed below. The achievement of maximal attainable age by any individual is a freak occurrence that is of very minor quantitative significance. The majority of animals die in their prime, if not in their extreme youth. Some concept of average age seems of greater significance, but to avoid ambiguity we must point out that there are two current meanings to the concept. The simplest to visualize is that of the age attained by a median individual. If we imagine a group of 1000 animals of a particular species born at the time instant t_0 and further imagine that we maintain surveillance over these animals until the last one has died, there will be a time when the 500th individual has just died. If we refer to this time instant as $t_{0 + md}$, the median age of our animals or the median life expectancy at birth is equal to the interval $(t_{0 + md} - t_0)$. For some animals the median life expectancy is surprisingly short. In mackerel, for example, the median life expectancy at the time of birth, taken as the time of fertilization of the extruded egg, is of the order of 12 hours, although a month-old mackerel has a very good chance of living three or four years. We therefore use another concept of average life that is called the "mean life expectancy." This is the number of years of life that will be lived by an average animal in a group.

Defining the number of individuals born alive at the instant t_0 as l_0 and defining the number of these individuals that are alive at a subsequent instant t_x as l_x, we can make a graph of l_x against time (Fig. 4-1). Survival and mortality data can be most simply discussed with reference to this survivorship graph.

There are four basic types of survivorship presented in Fig. 4-1, below. The mean life expectancy is calculated for any given age x as the area under the survivorship graph for all subsequent ages divided by the l_x value. That is, we compute the total number of animal years still available to the group at a particular time and divide that figure by the number of animals present at that time.

Notice that the median, mean, and maximum life expectancy at birth are almost equal for curve I. In curves I and II the mean

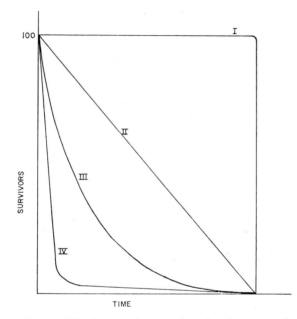

Fig. 4-1. The four simple types of survivorship curves. In type I, mortality is concentrated on the old animals. Type II is characterized by a constant number of deaths per unit time. Type III is found when the risk of death is constant with age. Type IV has mortality concentrated at the young stages.

life expectancy remaining for each individual decreases with age. Curve II represents a system in which a constant number of the animals die per unit time, regardless of the number remaining. Curve III represents a system in which a constant fraction of the animals alive die at each age. Mean life expectancy at any age remains constant throughout the life of the animal. Curve IV represents a population in which mortality mainly affects the young animals. In this case mean life expectancy of any individual increases with age. Median life expectancy is very short compared with the mean.

The type IV curve is probably the most common in nature, although natural populations in general are not identical with any one of these curves in shape. Typically different ages are susceptible to different sources of mortality, producing a survivorship curve that is a mixture of the various curves ideally possible. Most of the animals that have a distinctive larval stage followed by meta-morphosis into an adult condition have extremely high mortality in the young stages or in the transition from one mode of life to another. This group includes most fish, insects, crustacea, and coelenterates. Almost all animals that care for their young show high mortality rates at the ages of weaning and termination of parental care. For most animals in nature the rate of mortality is approximately constant once they reach adult life. If this rate is sufficiently high, the number of individuals that even approach the physiological limits are insignificant and for all practical purposes the latter part of the survivorship curve is of type III. Many fish populations (Ricker, 1958; Beverton and Holt, 1958), adult bird populations (Lack, 1954; Paynter, 1947), and the terrestrial phase of some salamanders (Organ, 1961) have type III survivorship curves when adult.

Occasionally the rate of mortality in a population is sufficiently low, or the causes of mortality are associated in such a way with the physiological condition of the animals that the degeneration familiar to us as aging can occur. These populations may have a dip in the survivorship curve in early life, followed by a period of very low mortality, followed by a period of rapid death—that is, a mixture of types I and IV. The survivorship curve of modern Western man is of this type, whereas that of ancient Rome or certain areas of our present world in which public health practices are relatively primitive is more like that of birds (type III).

A pattern very similar to that of modern man is found among Dall mountain sheep (Murie, 1944; Deevey, 1947), where the young animals seem less adept at escaping predators and the very old animals have difficulty with their teeth and jaws, so undermining their capacity to maintain a proper nutritive state that they, too, fall prey to wolves. Grazing animals, in general, are limited in the duration of their life by the wearing down of their teeth and, in the absence of unusual outbreaks of disease or predation, may be expected to follow the mountain sheep pattern of mortality. An extremely rectangular survivorship curve also occurs in insects that have a long larval life followed by a very short period of reproductive activity followed by death. Swammerdam studied the detailed anatomy of the May fly (Swammerdam, 1681) to demonstrate the infinite care used by the Creator in producing an organism of such inordinate complexity that is destined to live "but five hours" as an adult.

Thus far we have spoken of the survivorship curve as if it were a constant characteristic of a population or even a species. Although the general shape of the curve does not change very much, the actual duration of life and the details of curve shape are extremely sensitive to environmental conditions and to the sex and genotype of the individuals. Frank (1960) has demonstrated in the water flea, Daphnia, which we will meet frequently in this book, that duration of life varies in the laboratory with the number of animals kept in a container. He has further shown that altering the number of animals in the container approximately halfway through the life of a group of animals causes a shift in the shape of the survival curve from that moment on. Pearl (1928) found that vestigial winged fruit fly adults in the laboratory have a survivorship curve of type III whereas normal winged flies or vestigial winged flies in the absence of fly food have a survival curve of type I. In this case either a single gene change in the population or a single factor change in the environment could switch the shape of the survival curve from type I to type III. The explanation seems to be that in the absence of food both vestigial winged adults and normal adults live until they have exhausted their reserves and then die, creating a type I curve. In the presence of the sticky mess normally used as laboratory fruit fly food the vestigial winged flies, which must crawl over the food continually in order to eat, are subject to a constant risk of fouling; the normal winged flies are relatively immune to this risk.

In the laboratory, survivorship data can be readily acquired by isolating a group of animals of identical age and maintaining them until the last one is dead. In nature, however, acquisition of data from which survivorship data can be constructed often involves extreme ingenuity. Even though some animals can be conveniently

aged, by methods analogous to the aging of trees, there are ambiguities in the interpretation of the age data. For example, it has been
found that the teeth of many species of seals contain growth rings
similar to those found in trees. McLaren (1958), using tooth rings
and claw rings, which are apparently annual additions giving
accurate age up to nine years—at least in the Ringed seal—has been
able to present an excellent account of the biology of the Ringed
seal but is not able to construct a survivorship curve. Knowledge
of the age distribution of a population of living animals permits
reconstruction of the survivorship curve only if certain relatively
stringent assumptions are met. Particularly, it must be assumed
that the population size is constant, implying constant annual
reproduction. The death rate at each age must be constant from
year to year. The population examined must be free of immigration
and emigration, or the immigration and emigration must be equally
balanced in age and number of animals. McLaren could show the
growth rate as a function of age in various localities but he could
not definitely assert that the above assumptions had been met for
any one locality.

The Dall mountain sheep data were derived from the number
of rings on the horns of skulls found in Mt. McKinley National
Park. The several hundred skulls were considered to be a repre-
sentative sample of the population over several years, and hence
the peculiarities of the death pattern of any one year were for the
most part eliminated. It had to be assumed that the rate of dis-
integration of the various skulls was independent of their age at
death and that no broad pattern of population increase or decrease
occurred during the period of skull accumulation. The collection
of skulls was then assumed to represent a group or cohort of animals
born at one particular time, and the number of individuals found
of any particular age was assumed to represent the number of
organisms in this cohort dying at that age. There were two samples
of skulls from two different periods. One of these samples, containing 608 skulls with a mean age at death of 7.09 years, was used
by Deevey (1947) to compute the survivorship curve. The procedure
was to multiply the number of skulls found in each age interval
—that is, 1 to 2, 3 to 4, 5 to 6 years—by 608/1000, the product being
the number dying at that age from a cohort of 1000, referred to
as $d_x \times 10^3$. The values for l_x for each age can now be determined

by starting with $l_0 = 1.000$ and subtracting d_0 to produce l_1—in this case .801—subtracting the observed d_1 from this value to produce l_2 and so on.

One of the most ingenious procedures for determining the survivorship of a population was that used by Edmondson (1944). He first dusted the surface of a pond with powdered carmine, which was used by the sessile rotifer Floscularia in constructing its tube. Edmondson returned one day later and dusted the same area with powdered charcoal, which, in turn, was used by the Floscularia in tube construction. It was possible to determine growth rates, reproduction rates, and mortality rates, and by an indirect procedure to make all these rates age specific.

By plotting the distance between the carmine line and the charcoal line against the initial height of the tube, it was possible to make a graph of the growth per 24 hours against size of the animals. By subtracting the size-specific growth rate per 24 hours from animals of each size repeatedly, it was possible to construct an age-size graph. The mortality at each age per 24 hours is then the number of dead animals of the appropriate size that have a carmine ring in the tube but not a charcoal ring. A check value is attainable from the dead animals that have both rings. Reproduction cannot be made age specific, but the total set per 24 hours on a Utricularia plant is equal to the number of rotifers that have a charcoal band but not a carmine band. The errors in the process make the method more interesting than the data, but as an example of ecologists' ingenuity, it is almost unrivaled. Implicit in the work of Edmondson is the assumption that the size-specific growth rates are themselves constant.

Occasionally reproduction is sufficiently seasonal and growth rate sufficiently great that animals born in different years can be distinguished by their size alone. On the assumption of constant reproductive rates and population size the survivorship curve can then be immediately derived from the number of animals at the various ages.

Populations with type III survivorship curves are relatively common and particularly convenient to work with since, if mortality rate is constant, log l_x will be a straight line when plotted against time. In fish populations, where age of individuals can be determined by counting the rings on scales or otoliths, fish caught commercially can 'be used to determine adult mortality rates and the adult survivorship curve if they conform to type III, even though the fishing equipment (nets, etc.) may not be taking a random sample of the population as a whole. As Beverton and Holt (1958) and Ricker (1958) have shown, the log of age frequency plotted against age is actually a straight line, at least for the older ages, in a variety of commercially significant fish. This may tend to be obscured by the rather violent fluctuations that fish populations may undergo in young survival from year to year. A fair estimate of the survivorship curve is obtained by extrapolating these lines into those ages that are not subject to being caught by fishing. The fishing process itself alters the mortality pattern to a varying degree and both Ricker, and Beverton and Holt discuss this problem in detail.

The absolute mean length of time lived by an animal is quite independent of the shape of the survivorship curve. It can probably be stated with fair certainty that the majority of species have a life expectancy at birth of one year or less. The life expectancy of Edmondson's rotifers was eight days at the time of settling (Edmondson, 1944). There is some evidence that in the temperate zone a few Daphnia in nature may overwinter under the ice and be the parents of the first spring generation (Brooks, 1946).

This short life expectancy not only applies to the small animals but is also valid for many of the more conspicuous ones. Among the estimates listed by Lack (1954) of the average life expectancy of birds that have been successfully fledged are 1.1 years for the English robin, 1.8 years for the song sparrow, and not more than three years for any birds except the swift, penguin, and albatross. These figures are an overestimate of life expectancy at birth since the percentage of young birds that reach the flying stage from an egg is not more than 80 percent in any species, with the exception of the house wren, the starling and English sparrow in America, and the swallow (*Hirunda rustica*), and falls below 60 percent in all species of open nested birds examined with the exception of the blackbird (*Turdus merula*) in the Shetlands.

The life expectancy data for birds are fairly good since birds are conspicuous animals and there are very highly organized banding programs in several countries. Only scattered reports exist for other animals, however. On the basis of available data, the life expectancy for birds seems not very different from that of most other animals, with the exception of the large herd animals like the Dall mountain sheep with a mean life expectancy at birth of approximately 7 years. McLaren's histograms for age distribution in populations of Ringed seal indicate a mean age of from two to five years for most regions, with a higher mean age of from seven to ten years, in regions of deeply indented coastline. Some specimens as old as 18 years or more were found.

The calculations and significance of life tables and survivorship have been most carefully developed for man, since they are of central importance to the life insurance business. Dublin, Lotka, and Spiegelman (1949) have recently summarized much of the human life table information and procedures. Since the animal data are usually so crude and the financial and scientific risks involved in misinterpretation are generally not very great, except in fishery management programs (see Ricker, 1958), most of the refinements used in actuarial analysis of human survivorship data are not needed. It is, however, of interest to point out briefly some of the problems.

If a survivorship curve is derived from human age-at-death data collected in a particular year—say 1950—the persons who died at age 60 in that year were born in 1890 and were therefore subject to the infant mortality rates prevalent at that time. There is every reason to believe that persons born in 1940 will not have the same death rate at age 60 as those born in 1890. The death rate of the 1940 group will determine the life insurance corporation profits in the future, however, much more than will that of the earlier group, for which more complete data are available. The job of the actuary therefore involves projection of secular age-specific death rate changes into the future. In this process it has been found that the change of death rates with time varies considerably at the different ages of man. The life expectancy of an eighty-year-old American today is not very different from that of an eighty-year-old in ancient Rome. In both cases the body runs down and death is likely to arise from a degenerative disease or the inability to repair traumatic body damage. Whereas the Roman eighty-year-old was less likely to receive first-class medical attention than the modern octogenarian, the latter, having been protected from many other sources of mortality all his life, is likely to be less tough than the ancient. A white American infant born today has a much better chance of surviving to the age of one year than did his counterpart in 1900 or an Egyptian baby of today. In 1900 a newborn American infant had 162 chances out of a thousand of dying in his first year; an American infant of today has a chance of less than 29 in a thousand of dying in the first year; and an Egyptian infant in 1955 had a chance of somewhat over 200 out of a thousand of dying before his first birthday.

In general, as infectious disease is being reduced as a cause of death, the degenerative diseases are becoming more important a source. The physiological capacity of man seems to set a limit beyond which medicine can extend life only a little.

Any change in the size of human and animal populations will alter the significance of age-at-death data. In an increasing population there will be a greater apparent death rate in the younger age categories. In a decreasing population, however, there will be a decreased apparent death rate in the younger age categories unless the data are suitably corrected to take account of the total number of individuals alive in each age category during the interval over which the deaths were recorded.

One of the most difficult things to determine about most animals is how many of them are alive at any particular time. This is true even of human census counts in urban areas, where it would seem a simple matter to go from door to door and elicit information from families. Age data as reported in censuses are notoriously inaccurate, with the obvious biases in favor of youth by middle-aged persons, of maturity by very young persons, and of even numbers by almost everyone. Extremely old persons tend to add a few years to their ages. Dates of birth are confused, particularly among illiterate or semiliterate people (Wolfenden, 1954).

Although animals are not deliberately deceptive they are even more difficult to census—except for those in laboratories or on farms—and data acquisition requires ingenuity. The danger in most direct counts is that the same animals are counted twice or are omitted entirely. This can sometimes be precluded by having a very large number of census takers move through an area simultaneously, reporting all animals seen within a specific distance of their line of march; or better, driving all the animals before them into an enclosure and counting them as they are released. This procedure works in some deer parks and game preserves, but usually it is impossible to gather a sufficiently large number of competent investigators at the same time and place.

Sampling procedures can be used for animals that cannot be conveniently herded but are conspicuous in all or part of their range. Sometimes animals cannot be seen but may be heard. This is particularly the case with birds, where the singing males can be taken as a rough estimate of the number of breeding pairs of birds in the area. Investigators may walk through an area to count the animals they see within a specified distance of their path and then multiply this area by an appropriate factor to give an approximation of the number in the entire area. This method assumes homogeneity of distribution within the area and complete reports of the animals in the observed subarea.

Out of casual curiosity I estimated the number of earthworms on the surface of my backyard lawn, at night, by walking barefoot over the lawn in several transects and counting the number of worms that pulled out from under my feet. Multiplying this number by the ratio of the area covered by my feet to that of total lawn area, I estimated that on a spring night upward of 300 earthworms occupied the lawn. I would not stake my reputation on that number but it gives an idea of the method. If an investigator is really very determined to find the total number of organisms present at a particular time he may kill all of the animals and count them. This method is most often used in fish ponds or sections of lakes and rivers in which dynamite or poisons can be used to kill the fish.

Individual males or individual pairs of a species may maintain definite territories in which they are relatively conspicuous, and so may be readily counted. Unfortunately, in many of these species (as, for example, red-winged blackbirds, bower birds, and herring gulls) there are often many nonbreeding individuals that do not have possession of a territory and are not at all conspicuous.

A less direct method of counting is by a dilution technique. A group of animals is captured, marked in some way, and released. Population size can be estimated on the basis of the following requirements: (1) if the marked individuals are a random sample of the population, (2) if they disperse at random through the entire population, (3) if the marking procedure does not damage them,

(4) if none of the marks are eradicated or lost, (5) if the likelihood of marked individuals being captured again is independent of their having once been captured, and (6) if mortality is negligible between the time of original release of marked individuals and the time of recapture. The size of the population is estimated as the number of marked individuals initially released multiplied by total individuals caught in a second sampling divided by marked individuals in the second sample. Various procedures for assessing the importance of the several assumptions are available and the statistical confidence limits of the final estimate of population size can, in some cases, be explicitly stated (Ricker, 1958).

In summary, the survivorship curve of each species in nature more or less maintains its general form, although environmental and genetic factors may alter the shape somewhat. Most animals in nature are capable of living much longer than they actually do. The causes of death are widely various for each species and each cause may act unequally on the different age classes of animals.

Determination of the actual number of animals in any population in nature is a difficult process, usually involving certain assumptions that may or may not be verifiable. Rough estimates are possible in many cases and very good estimates are occasionally possible.

chapter five ▸ # Reproduction
▸
▸ and Increase

We must ask the same kind of questions about reproduction
that we asked about death; for example, what is an appropriate
measure of reproduction? The production of young can either be
centered in one short interval of the female's life or be spread over
a very long period. Most animals do not reproduce continually;
rather, the production of young is spaced at intervals, with varying time between each birth. The closest thing to continual reproduction is probably found among the queens in termite colonies,
where one or more eggs per minute are produced day in and day
out over many years. At an opposite extreme are the cicadas that
spend 13 or 17 years as larvae and concentrate all of their reproduction into one short spring. The simplest measure of reproduction is litter size, which may range from that of the large
herbivorous mammals like elephants in which twins are unknown,
to the fishes like salmon in which tens of thousands of eggs at least
are produced at a spawning, to the oyster in which literally millions
of eggs may be released at each spawning by one female. The number of young per litter may vary within the same species from place
to place and environment to environment and time to time.
Whereas the armadillo always has quadruplets and gulls always have
a three-egg clutch, many animals show considerable variability in
the size of a litter. In man, one, two, and even three young at a
time are relatively common, although single births predominate.
In Daphnia the litters may have anywhere from one to 150 eggs.

Despite this enormous variation in reproductive patterns, each female adult animal alive now—in every species, in almost every location—will be replaced by precisely one female alive a generation from now. If this were not the case, the size of animal populations would be changing permanently and strikingly at a much greater rate than any existing evidence indicates. We can summarize this remarkably simple conclusion in the form of a survivorship distribution for females in which l_0 is taken as equal to one and m_x, a column of fecundity values, is defined as the number of female young produced by an average female during the interval of age $x - \frac{1}{2}$, $x + \frac{1}{2}$. It must be the case in the steady state that $\sum_0^\infty l_x m_x = 1$, regardless of the shape of the survivorship curve or of the curve of fecundity with age, and regardless of any of the absolute numerical values involved. That is, each single female must replace herself with one and only one female during her lifetime. If the probability of survival is particularly small, the number of young produced by the few survivors must be correspondingly great. If a female has many opportunities to breed, she can produce correspondingly few young at each breeding period.

The summation of number of young produced during each time interval by each live female, expressed as $\sum l_x m_x$, is also referred to as R_0, the replacement rate of the population. $R_0 = 1$ implies that the population replaces itself precisely every generation; $R_0 > 1$ implies that the population is increasing; and $R_0 < 1$ implies that the population is decreasing. Since we have assumed constancy of the l_x and m_x distributions, the actual number of animals present cannot, in our present discussion, influence the survival or fecundity of any one animal. This assumption is, in fact, false; and we will have to return to the concept of R_0 when we are free of the assumption.

The difference between life expectancy in nature and in captivity and the difference in fecundity per female as a function of the environment indicate what was already obvious to Plato, Rashi, and Linnaeus;[1] namely, that under suitable conditions populations

---

[1] These men are mentioned not because they were the only ones to have developed the concept but to show that at least every fifteen hundred years through recorded history the concept has arisen.

of organisms can increase at an exponential, logarithmic, or Malthusian rate. Malthus (1798) stated it as follows:

> Through the animal and vegetable kingdoms, nature has scattered the seeds of life abroad with the most profuse and liberal hand. She has been comparatively sparing in the room and the nourishment necessary to rear them. The germs of existence contained in this spot of earth, with ample food and ample room to expand in, would fill millions of worlds in the course of a few thousand years. Necessity, that imperious all-pervading law of nature, restrains them within the prescribed bounds. The race of plants, and the race of animals shrink under this great restrictive law. . . . Among plants and animals its effects are waste of seed, sickness, and premature death.

This waste of seed, sickness, and premature death is what we have seen in the shape of natural survivorship curves. Any amelioration of the environment that increases the likelihood of survival in a particular population above that required for the maintenance of $R_0 = 1$ will result in population increase. On a short-term basis such ameliorations of the environment do occur and are accompanied by increase. The simplest example is the arrival of spring in temperate climates, which is an occasion for the production of young by the majority of species of plants and animals. How many organisms of each species are present during the summer will depend in part on how fully the populations could take advantage of the temporary beneficence of the spring—that is, on the populations' maximum potential rate of increase. For populations living in a completely constant world the potential rate of increase matters only at the time immediately after the initial invasion of this world. After the newly opened environment has been occupied, other qualities of the organism become of primary significance in determining whether a population will hold possession of it. The distinction is somewhat analogous to the temperamental difference between pioneering human societies and societies in completely settled countries. Just as certain men live for the rigors of the frontier, certain species are adapted to survival in temporary and unstable ecological niches in which rate of population expansion is of great importance.

Occasionally a species is put into a completely new ecological situation that permits it to expand at an amazingly rapid rate.

An outstanding example is the expansion of the striped bass (*Roccus saxatilis*) population on the American Pacific coast. Merriman (1941) reports:

> In 1879 and 1881 a number of yearling bass were seined in New Jersey, taken across the continent in tanks by train, and planted in San Francisco Bay. A total of only 435 Striped Bass survived the rigors of these two trips. Yet, by 1889, . . . they were caught in gill nets and offered for sale, and in 1899 the commercial net catch alone was 1,234,000 pounds.

A millionfold increase in the weight of this population in twenty years would be an underestimate. At the same time the population of striped bass on the East coast was constant or declining slightly. It should be emphasized again, however, that most transplantations of animals are completely unsuccessful and even the relatively successful ones do not generally show the explosive increase shown by the bass.

Let us imagine a population that is suddenly presented with the opportunity for exponential increase. Initially the number of animals in the first age category will increase, while the number of animals in the older age categories will remain the same as when the population was static. Little by little all of the age categories will show an increase as the survivors from the enlarged initial category grow older. As more animals enter the reproductive categories more and more newborn will be produced. After a few generations, however, the total number of animals will increase at a fairly steady rate. If we plot the number of animals in the population against time we will find an exponential increase curve and, if we plot the natural logarithm of number of animals against time, we will find a straight line. This can be expressed by the equation

$$N_0 e^{rt} = N_t$$

where N_0 is the number of animals in the population at some arbitrary initial time, N_t is the number of animals in the population t time units later, r is the instantaneous rate of increase (which would correspond to the instantaneous interest rate in a compound interest problem), and e is the base of the natural logarithms. Lotka (1956) has shown as a theorem that the relative number of animals represented by animals of a particular age approaches constancy as the rate of increase approaches its final value.

Since the population as a whole is increasing at the rate r and the relative number of animals in each age category is staying constant, each separate age category is increasing at the same rate; that is, for all ages, x, the number of animals of that age at time t, is related to the number of animals of that age at time $(t + 1)$ by

$$n_{x,(t+1)} = n_{x,t} \, e^{rt}$$

or

$$n_{x,(t+1)} \, e^{-rt} = n_{x,t}$$

where $n_{x,t}$ is the number of animals of age x alive at time t and $n_{x,(t+1)}$ is the number of animals of age x alive at time $(t + 1)$. Consider the newborn animals, $l_{0,t}$, in a population that has reached this stable age distribution at time t. The animals designated as $l_{0,t}$ are the offspring of the breeding animals that reproduced in the interval t. Let us examine the parents of $l_{0,t}$.

If we arbitrarily set $l_{0,t} = 1$, then at time $(t - 1)$ there were e^{-r} individuals of age 0 and l_1 of these have survived to provide the $l_1 e^{-r}$ individuals of age 1 alive at time t. At time $(t - 2)$ there were e^{-2r} individuals born and they are represented by $l_2 e^{-2r}$ individuals at time t. In general, at time $(t - x)$ there were e^{-rx} individuals born and at time t they are represented by $l_x e^{-rx}$ individuals. The number of individuals born to the animals alive at time t is $\sum l_x m_x e^{-rx}$, which equals $l_{0,t}$. We have already set $l_{0,t}$ equal to one, and so $1 = \sum l_x m_x e^{-rx}$. This equation has several interesting properties. To permit a real population to increase until it reaches its constant rate of increase is a very difficult thing to do with most organisms. Our equation permits us to calculate the stable age distribution $(l_x e^{-rx})$ once we know the final rate of increase r and permits us to calculate r from the survivorship and fecundity data, which are relatively easy to obtain. Also, since r is an instantaneous rate, it permits comparison between animals that have widely different absolute lengths of life and generation times. Notice that R_0 was the increase per generation and therefore could not be compared as well from animal to animal.

Given the $l_x m_x$ data, r is calculated by a trial-and-error process that is nicely outlined by Leslie and Park (1949), Andrewartha and Birch (1954), Frank et al. (1957), and others. When $R_0 = 1$, $r = 0$; that is, when the population is not increasing there is no increase rate. For an increasing population, $e^{rT} = R_0$, where T is the generation time; we mentioned generation time before but only briefly since it is a very difficult concept to define except by the above equation.

The diminution of future population increase produced by removing a single animal of a given age from a population may be termed the reproductive value of that individual. If there is a very high mortality prior to the reproductive period, the reproductive value of each surviving immature individual must be considerably greater than 1 to maintain age distribution constancy. Once the reproductive period begins, each reproducing animal diminishes the ratio of its future offspring to its past offspring as it grows older, until at the end of the reproductive period the reproductive value of an organism in an asocial population is zero. The greater the value of r and the longer the population has been growing since the birth of the animal, the greater must be its reproductive value if its proportionate contribution is to stay constant. Fisher (1958) combines these properties in the equation

$$\frac{v_x}{v_0} = \frac{e^{rx}}{l_x} \int_x^{\infty} e^{-rt} l_t m_t dt$$

where v_x is the reproductive value at age x, v_0 is the reproductive value at birth, and the other symbols are the same as those used previously. As Fisher points out, a postreproductive organism may have a reproductive value by contributing aid and comfort to its descendants, as, for example, an old female elk that contributes to the survival of the group by her knowledge of forage trails or a grandmother who baby sits with the grandchildren. This type of reproductive value is not expressed in the equation.

The concept of reproductive value is of particular interest from an evolutionary standpoint since the age of peak reproductive value is also the age of peak sensitivity to natural selection. The freshman textbook truism that "ontogeny recapitulates phylogeny" simply states that those ages of an animal that have a low reproductive value change relatively little under natural selection and those ages that either have a high reproductive value themselves, or, since ontogenetic time is unidirectional, are older than animals with a maximal reproductive value, change rather rapidly in evolution. There are also consequences for short-time population growth that we will discuss later. Reproductive value curves as a function of age are presented in Fig. 5-1 for a human and an insect population.

Smith (1954) collected several of the computed values of r then available for various species and prepared a graph showing the relation between r, R_0, and T for these species (Fig. 5-2). Notice that any two of these values determine the third but there is no necessary relation on theoretical grounds between all three. Smith

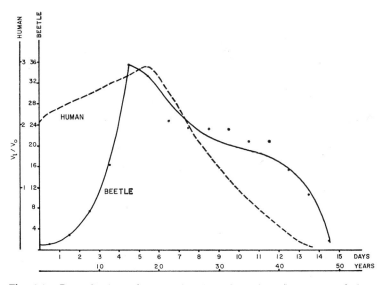

Fig. 5-1. Reproductive value as a function of age for a human population, redrawn from Fisher (1958), and a beetle population (*Calandra oryzae*). The beetle reproductive values were calculated from the data of Birch (1948).

found that small organisms had higher values of r and shorter generation time in general. There is a strong taxonomic component in this result since most of the smaller organisms are unicellular or acellular. Later results, such as those of Frank *et al.* (1957), fit nicely into Smith's graph, and there is every reason to consider that the generalized inverse relation between r and body size is valid.

Smith concludes from this relation that r is a measure of the expected harshness of the animals' environment and that, compared to small animals, large animals live in a benign world. This may be interpreted to mean that by increasing the size per individual a species outgrows a series of sources of mortality. Smith considers that physical factors such as diffusion are of greater significance and therefore greater potential danger in the life of a very small animal than in that of a big one. It might be added that whether a partic-

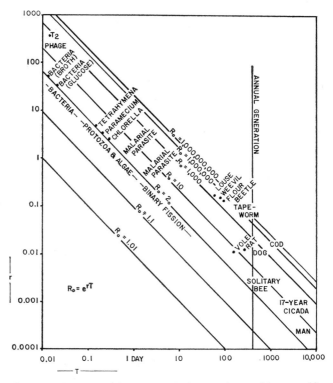

Fig. 5-2. The relation between intrinsic rate of natural increase (r), generation time (the abscissa) and increase per generation (R_0) for a variety of animals. (Adapted and redrawn from Smith, 1954.)

ular environmental change is catastrophic depends in part on the size of the animal.

Although $r = 0$ always holds when a population has filled its environment, the expansion into the environment is impossible unless physical conditions, in the absence of biological crowding, permit l_x and m_x to be great enough to make r greater than zero. During World War II the Australian government was prevented by enemy submarine activity from sending grain to Europe at the normal rate and was therefore concerned with infestation of stored Australian grain by various species of grain beetle. By experimentally determining the effect of temperature and humidity on l_x and m_x for two species of flour beetle, Birch (1948) found that with certain sets of temperature and humidity r fell below 0 for each species. An r value of 0 marks the limit of the possible ecological range of a species. He found further that one species, *Rhizopertha dominica,* could increase at higher temperatures and lower humidity than the other, *Callandyra oryzae,* which in turn was more resistant to cold. The expected geographical distribution of these two species in nature corresponded roughly with the predictions from this result; that is, *Rhizopertha dominica* occurred at higher latitudes in Australia than *Callandyra oryzae.* The parameter r need not, however, have any direct relation with the maintainable steady-state population size.

Rareness and commonness are not correlated with r for animals as a whole. The nature of the selective processes involved in determining the value of r for any particular species is not simple. Selection favors those members of any population that leave the greatest number of eventual descendants. Under some circumstances a greater immediate reproductive potential—that is, a higher value of r—may lead to an actual diminution of eventual descendants. Selective advantage accrues to a higher value of r only in species that normally live in temporary environments that they never fully saturate.

Consider the hypothetical situation of a species with an extremely high value of r but a very low tolerance to food shortage. This situation would be selectively advantageous during a good food period but would result in widespread mortality during a period of low food. A somewhat lower value of r for the same species might permit sufficiently greater survival in a low food year to more than counteract the slow increase during a good food year. In fact, there is ample evidence that r has often been reduced during the course of evolution (Slobodkin and Richman, 1956). A careful analysis of the dependence of r on various physiological properties has been made by Cole (1954a) following the method of Thompson and Soper (1931).

To summarize the results of Cole's analysis, in general, reduction of age of first reproduction, increase in litter size, and increase in longevity all tend to increase r. The effect of increased numbers of litters per female lifetime is surprisingly small if the initial reproductive age is very young. In particular, in a species in which reproduction first occurs at some arbitrary age x and the females are immortal, the effect on r of an infinitely prolonged reproductive life per female, with new litters coming at intervals of x years, is equivalent to adding one animal to the initial litter at age x. If, however, initial reproduction is at a later age, but litters are still produced every x years, increase in longevity becomes more significant in increasing r. The effect on r of litter size and age at first reproduction is greater the smaller the size of the individual litter.

With the advance of technology and consequent economic advantage to the individual of technical training, there is commonly a delay in marriage age in man, the intervening time being filled by the period of schooling. This has a very strong depressing effect on the rate of population increase if there is a correlation between the ages of husband and wife. The early marriage trend in this country has effectively increased the American r in a way that does not, as a rule, result in any one family being excessively large. A woman who gives birth to a set of twins at the age of 19, and subsequently gives birth to one other child, contributes as much to the future population of America as does a woman who produces five children, but whose age at the birth of the initial child was 30. Stating the same thing in a somewhat different way, in an animal like man, in which the litter size is normally one, the number of births per female lifetime is in general of less significance in determining the reproductive potential of the population than is the age at initial reproduction. To my knowledge there is no strong sociological objection on the part of any religious or ethnic group to a somewhat delayed marriage, and this delaying of marriage may be a more satisfactory way to reduce human population increase than religiously or culturally objectionable contraceptive procedures.

It is quite obvious that the effect of selection on r will vary widely from animal to animal. If an animal has a very large litter size, as, for example, an oyster, it might be expected that natural selection would be more likely to increase litter size than to increase longevity of each female; the addition of one egg to the several million already present would have the same effect on r as infinite female reproductive life. An animal like man, which normally has only one young in a litter, faces severe physiological problems if the litter size is increased. Selection for increasing r will be expected to result in an early onset of reproductive activity and a long reproductive life in species that have very small litters.

In summary, if we assume that the physiological properties of individual animals remain constant with time we find that the population will come to a steady state. This steady state will always involve constancy of age distribution and reproductive rate distribution. For certain very limited situations, in which the l_x and m_x distributions have a very precise relation to each other so that $R_0 = 1$, the steady state will be characterized by constancy of population size. If these conditions are not met, the population will either increase or decrease and after sufficient time has elapsed the rate of increase or decrease will itself approach a constant value, r, the intrinsic rate of natural increase. For each set of physical conditions there exists a unique value of r for each species. (We are implicitly assuming genetic homogeneity in each population.)

The geographical distribution of each species is controlled, at the limit, by the range of physical conditions that permit a positive value of r and in at least one case knowledge of these conditions permits prediction of geographical range. The rate of increase is generally larger for very small organisms and this is probably related to the environmental instability faced by these organisms. Physiological properties of each species are intimately related to its r value and any evolutionary change in r implies changes in litter size, age at initial reproduction, or longevity, or some combination of these. The amount of physiological change necessary to produce a given change in r will depend on the initial physiological properties of the organisms.

chapter six ‣ Simple Changes
in Populations

We will now release our restriction on the populations and consider the course of events when a small number of animals enters a suitable ecological niche. As we have seen, there are extremely complex interactions occurring in the natural world. Any attempt to control or even measure the physical and biological parameters of nature will be extremely expensive and the naturalness of the world will itself be destroyed by the measuring and controlling process. In the laboratory, however, model situations can be constructed that agree more or less closely with various aspects of the natural ecological world. To the degree that ecological questions can be asked in such a way that the implicit assumptions underlying the question are empirically clear, there is hope of constructing an experimental model to answer the questions or test the assumptions. Experimental models lend themselves to quantitative expression more easily than field investigations, and those questions that can be mathematically formulated are the most valuable problems for laboratory experiments. As laboratory experiments become more complex and as the theory developed from them becomes richer it becomes possible to construct theoretical statements testable by field observations. These theoretical statements may themselves be fairly complex, but if they are properly formulated their validity is testable by relatively simple and inexpensive field data. A good theory of this sort, which is found valid in the field by a critical test, constitutes a description of the natural world that has more predictive value than a simpler but more "natural" theory based on field evidence alone. Just as the relation between electricity and other forms of energy applies wherever energy is found, although it was developed by an experimental and theoretical analysis of very simplified laboratory systems, so an ecological law does not owe its validity to its indoor or outdoor origin, but rather to its predictive value when confronted with actual problems.

Without field observations the laboratory studies are undirected and uninteresting. Without laboratory experiments the process of interpreting field data is excessively slow and costly. The interest of all ecologists is the prediction and comprehension of nature, but since the techniques and skills required for laboratory work and field work occasionally differ there was, at one time, an unfortunate lack of communication between the two groups. In the past few years communication has been reopened and the general problems of ecology are now coming into focus very rapidly. We will attempt here to present the ecological theory that has been built largely from laboratory results and then examine this theory in the light of field data.

In order to run an experimental population study it must be possible to maintain the animals in a laboratory. Surprisingly few animals are amenable to laboratory culture on the population level. Among the aquatic invertebrates, which have occupied most of my experimental time, it is found that the easiest animals to culture are the ones that live in the most polluted, stagnant, and generally filthiest natural environments. The organisms that are customarily found in the open, free water of lakes or in swift-flowing streams or the open ocean usually die when brought into a closed container in the laboratory. The vast majority of invertebrate animals have never been successfully raised under controlled conditions, and quite often the laboratory cultures require additives that are not chemically defined. Sheep manure, for example, and water extracts of boiled mud, dried yeast, dried blood, embryo juice, and similar refugees from a medieval pharmacopoeia are very common among culture medium ingredients. Any attempt to maintain an aquatic organism free of these chemical monstrosities is likely to be so difficult and complex as to make the additional problem of mode of interaction between animals in a constant environment almost secondary in importance. Small terrestrial organisms that might be useful for this type of study are equally difficult to maintain, especially if they refuse to be satisfied with relatively stable food like dry yeast or flour and insist on fresh plants or a living diet. Blood-sucking forms can be kept with relative ease by sufficiently dedicated experimentalists.

It might be assumed that zoological gardens would immediately acquire information on population interaction between organisms, but zoological gardens and public aquariums are so fully occupied attending to the wants of their animals that possible interactions between populations of these animals are certainly beyond their scope and interest. In fact, the larger and better zoos will specialize in keeping animals that are difficult to maintain in a live condition. The platypus, koala bear, and panda have particularly delicate tastes that must be catered to at major expense and a great deal of trouble.

Even if an animal can be maintained in the laboratory, this does not ensure its suitability for population experiments. Certain animals are almost impossible to census, even in a restricted environment. This is particularly true of insects that are either fast moving or have a strong preference for crevices, or both. Moreover, it is not practical to use animals with excessively long generation times. Larger terrestrial organisms are, in general, as long lived as the average research grant and are therefore extremely difficult to maintain under controlled conditions for a sufficient length of time to permit determination of steady-state values; and, in the extreme, as the organisms grow larger their life expectancy begins to approach the working life expectancy of the experimenter himself.

Animals are chosen for population experiments either because they are particularly convenient as objects for study or because they have considerable scientific or economic significance aside from their population dynamics. For most of my own work, I have used small Cladocera, either *Daphnia pulex* or *Daphnia obtusa*. These were chosen because of their simple dietary requirements, their partheno-genetic reproduction, and the fact that the small species of Daphnia fit conveniently into a standard drugstore medicine dropper and can therefore be counted much more easily than the large ones that tend to get crushed when drawn into a dropper. Of course, there are many other animals that have been maintained in the laboratory, but very few others have been maintained for sufficiently long periods and under sufficiently controlled conditions to make some analysis of the population pattern possible.

A great deal of work on the pests inhabiting stored starches such as grain or flour or beans has been done (Park, 1955; Utida, 1957), and studies have been made of blowflies, using bullock brain as a food (Nicholson, 1957). Populations of fruit flies have been studied primarily because of their genetic interest, although their medium is extremely complex (Bodenheimer, 1938). Occasional studies have been made of small rodent populations, but as a rule the space required for adequate replication is not available.

Some of the pioneering work in population dynamics has been done on microorganisms. They are, however, too simple to serve by themselves as meaningful models of nature. Moreover, most of the studies have used unrenewed media, where, for example, sugar solution or other nutrient broth is inoculated with a small number of protozoans or bacteria and the container is sealed. This creates the difficulty of differentiating between exhaustion of the initial energy content of the media and growth patterns of the population itself. (A careful analysis of the types of culture media relative to the pattern of energy inflow has been made by Smith [1952].)

Despite the problems inherent in such population studies and the consequent paucity of experiments, enough work has been done on a sufficiently diversified group of organisms to give some indication of the general complexity of population growth. The simplest models of population growth are those derived from the logistic or sigmoid curve and its various ramifications. We will call this type of theory "logistic theory" and will begin our discussion with it, later moving to more complex and realistic models and experiments.

Let us assume a limited volume of space that meets the physical requirements for the ecological niche of some particular species and further assume that food or some other sort of energy and mineral nutrient supply is passing through this space at some constant rate. Two equilibrium positions are possible for such a space. The less interesting of these is the unstable equilibrium that occurs when organisms are excluded from entry into the space. A tightly closed garbage pail in the summer is in this condition with reference to flies and a screened porch full of people is in this condition with reference to mosquitoes. In either case the equilibrium is upset by opening the container. The second equilibrium position is that which exists in a container that is so saturated with animals that no further increase will occur. (This case meets the previously discussed condition that the mean value of R_0 is equal to 1 at saturation.)

The logistic or sigmoid curve, developed by Verhulst and later used extensively by Pearl and others, is an elementary attempt to describe the history of a population in such a space between the time the first colonists arrive and the time of saturation. The reproductive and mortality rates of the individual animals in the population depend to some degree on the interaction between the animals themselves, whether or not this interaction is mediated through a change in one or more of the physiologically significant features of the environment. It is to be expected that the population will initially increase very rapidly with as close an approximation to the intrinsic maximum rate of natural increase, r, as is permitted by the age structure. As the environment becomes crowded the rate of increase per animal diminishes in proportion to the crowding until, finally, the increase ceases entirely.

In order to preserve mathematical simplicity, several implicit assumptions are made in the construction of the logistic curve. These are:

(1) All the animals in the population have identical ecological properties; that is, for example, all animals are equally likely to die or give birth or eat or be eaten. This effectively discards the concept of age structure, which we discussed in the previous chapter. The number of animals in the population is then simply designated by a single symbol, N. Occasionally N is used in referring to the population size in units of mass rather than as an enumeration of the number of animals.

(2) All the animals in the population respond instantaneously to alterations in their environment and, in particular, the rate of change of population size is a function of the present population size, not of the past history of the population. If you have ever waited for a skinned knee to heal or taken two weeks to recover from a cold it is obvious to you that organisms do not respond instantaneously. Various time lags in response exist and we will discuss them below. The point of this assumption is that it permits

the population change to be represented by the simple equation

$$\frac{dN}{dt} = f(N)$$

without introducing complex time functions into the right-hand term.

(3) There is some constant upper limit to population size in any particular situation, and the rate of increase of the population at any particular time is linearly proportional to the difference between the population size at that time and this upper limit. We will later have to modify this concept of a fixed upper limit to take account of various oscillatory phenomena, all of which are intimately related to the first two assumptions.

These assumptions can be conveniently embodied in an equation

$$\frac{dN}{dt} = rN \left(\frac{K - N}{K} \right)$$

or

$$\frac{dN}{dt} = rN - \frac{rN^2}{K}$$

where r is the intrinsic rate of natural increase in the absence of crowding and K is the number of animals, or the mass of animals, present at the saturation point. Since, as already noted by Archimedes (D'Arcy Thompson, 1943), any system that starts in one state and ends in another must pass through all intermediate states in the process, and since all experimental populations can be made to start at a relatively small size and terminate at a larger size, it is found that the logistic curve can be fitted fairly well to at least the initial portions of most population growth curves. It is one of the simplest possible expressions that will have the appropriate properties of an unstable equilibrium at $N = 0$ and a stable equilibrium at only one other value ($N = K$) and will provide for continuous decrease of growth rate per animal as the stable equilibrium value is approached.

In exchange for the unrealistic assumptions about age structure and the timing of responses we now can conveniently release our previous restriction that insisted that death and reproduction for each species stayed absolutely constant.

chapter seven

Competition between Species

Using the logistic equation, we can begin to make statements about the interaction between species by assuming that all of the species concerned are growing according to an equation of logistic form, differing only in the constants r and K and in the constants that describe the interaction between the different species. Despite the arbitrary restrictions and assumptions we will find that the conclusions derived from this theory are in very good agreement with natural field data, particularly with regard to the distribution of number and kinds of animals in space. This will be discussed at length later.

We start by developing the case in which two species are simultaneously introduced into an experimental space. Each species will have its own saturation value, determined by growing it alone. These saturation values will be designated by K_1 and K_2 respectively. Each species will also have its own rate of increase, r_1 and r_2 respectively. Designating our two species as N_1 and N_2, the inhibitory effect of one individual of species N_1 on its own species is $1/K_1$, where K_1 is the saturation level of N_1 alone; its inhibitory effect on species N_2 will have some other value, say β/K_2. Similarly, the effect of one individual of N_2 on the growth of species N_2 is $1/K_2$; its effect on N_1 is given by α/K_1. The simultaneous growth of the two species can now be indicated as

$$\frac{dN_1}{dt} = r_1 N_1 \frac{K_1 - N_1 - \alpha N_2}{K_1}$$

$$\frac{dN_2}{dt} = r_2 N_2 \frac{K_2 - N_2 - \beta N_1}{K_2}$$

We will refer to this equation system and its consequences as the Gause model of interspecific competition (Gause, 1935) or simply as the Gause model. This system is at equilibrium when

$$\frac{dN_1}{dt} = \frac{dN_2}{dt} = 0$$

The equilibrium is uninteresting if r_1, r_2, K_1, or K_2 equal zero. In the nonempty case all values of N_1 for which dN_1/dN_2 equal zero must lie on the line $N_1 = K_1 - \alpha N_2$. If this is plotted on a graph whose coordinates are N_1 and N_2, the N_1 intercept will be K_1 and the N_2 intercept will be K_1/α. The corresponding zero isocline for species N_2 has an N_2 intercept of K_2 and an N_1 intercept of K_2/β. If N_2 is represented on the ordinate and N_1 on the abscissa, all possible combinations of N_1 and N_2 will cross the N_1 zero isocline vertically and the N_2 isocline horizontally.

The possible outcome of competition for species that are forced to coexist in a restricted space can now be determined graphically. Four cases are possible:

Case 1: Either N_1 or N_2 will be the sole survivor depending on initial concentration:

$$\alpha > \frac{K_1}{K_2} \quad \text{and} \quad \beta > \frac{K_2}{K_1}$$

Case 2: Coexistence of the two species:

$$\alpha < \frac{K_1}{K_2} \quad \text{and} \quad \beta < \frac{K_2}{K_1}$$

Case 3: N_1 is always the sole survivor:

$$\alpha < \frac{K_1}{K_2} \quad \text{and} \quad \beta > \frac{K_2}{K_1}$$

Case 4: N_2 is always the sole survivor:

$$\alpha > \frac{K_1}{K_2} \quad \text{and} \quad \beta < \frac{K_2}{K_1}$$

These cases are diagrammatically represented in Fig. 7-1.

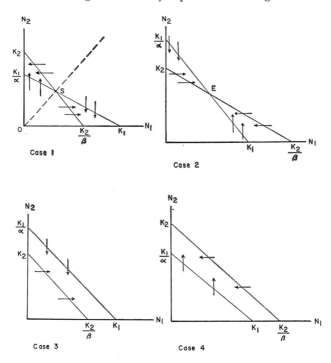

Fig. 7-1. Competitive interaction between pairs of species. In each case the lines K_1, K_1/α and K_2, K_2/β represent the saturation values for species N_1 and N_2 respectively. As indicated by the short arrows, neither species can increase above its saturation line. Below its saturation line each species will increase. These are four cases:

Case 1: Unstable equilibrium is possible at point S, but it is to be expected that one and only one species will survive. Which species survives depends on whether the initial mixture of species lies to the right or left of the line OS.

Case 2: Stable equilibrium occurs at point E. Initial concentrations of the two species are irrelevant.

Case 3: Species N_1 will always win in competition since the region K/α, K_2, K_2/β, K_1 is below the saturation level of N_1 but above the saturation level of N_2.

Case 4: Species N_2 will always win in competition since the region K_2, K_1/α, K_1, K_2/β is below the saturation level of N_2 but above the saturation level of N_1.

We can examine Case 1 more carefully by referring to Fig. 7-1. Above or on the line K_1, K_1/α species N_1 is unable to increase. The arrows therefore cross this line vertically, indicating that species N_2 is still free to alter. Above or on the line K_2, K_2/β species N_2 is unable to increase, and so the arrows crossing the isocline are arranged horizontally. In the triangle K_1, S, K_2/β species N_2 is above its saturation level and species N_1 is not; thus if a mixture of species N_1 and N_2 is present in this triangle species N_2 will diminish while species N_1 will continue to increase until only it remains.

In the triangle K_2, S, K_1/α the reverse situation will hold, since N_1 is above its saturation level in this region and N_2 is not. The line OS and its extension divides the possible initial mixtures of species N_1 and N_2 into two distinct sets. Any mixture above line OS will eventually leave N_2 victorious; any mixture below line OS will eventually leave only N_1 as the survivor. This case can be represented in a three-dimensional model (Fig. 7-2). The entire surface is represented as a hill with a ridge OS and two spoon-shaped tilted hollows representing the two triangles K_2, S, K_1/α and K_1, S, K_2/β. The area O, K_1/α, S, K_2/β is a mound-shaped structure with the curvature reversing sign at the isoclines. The rate of change of population size is proportional to the height of the landscape at that point; the direction of change is determined by the shape of the surface. The unstable equilibrium point S is a crest in the middle of a pair of spoon-shaped valleys. The valleys are tilted so that the edge farther from the origin is lower than that nearer the origin. If a ball is placed at any point on this topographic model it will roll in the direction that would be taken by a point representing a mixture of the two species N_1 and N_2.

Case 2 can be represented by a topographic model (see Fig. 7-2) consisting of two mounds separated by two spoon-shaped valleys whose floors dip down at the center to form a hollow or pit, E, which is the equilibrium mixture for the two species. In this case E is a stable equilibrium point or "knot" and any initial mixture will eventually arrive there (Fig. 8-1, p. 77). At this point the rate of change of both species is zero and neither species is absent. Elimination of one species would increase the equilibrium value of the other but neither one can eliminate the other by competition.

The topographic models for Cases 3 and 4 are (see Fig. 7-2) much simpler and can be represented by a single hollow valley

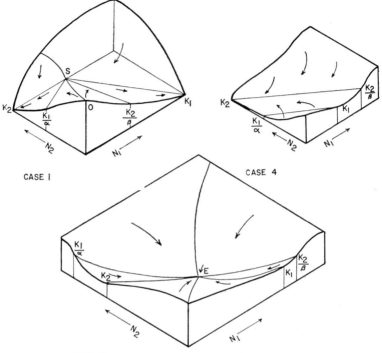

Fig. 7-2. Interspecific competition represented as a 3-dimensional model. Any initial mixture of two species will move over the N_1, N_2 plane as a ball would roll on the appropriate model.

between two hills with the deepest part of the valley at the point K_1 in Case 3 and at the point K_2 in Case 4.

It is of interest to examine also the biological properties of the system as well as the formal mathematical ones. The implication of the model is that the two species are utilizing the same physical space but not in the same way. In Case 1, for example, it is implied that some metabolite is excreted by each species, which, if present in sufficient concentration, will inhibit the growth of the other species more severely than that of its producer. Both species do more to damage the environment for the competing species than they do to destroy environmental opportunities for their own species. Note that behavioral activities that frighten other species more than they frighten members of their own species would have essentially the same effect as metabolites. The term "metabolites" is used here in a very broad sense as a generalized byproduct of metabolism. In Case 2 both species are more damaging to themselves than to the competing species and therefore are not completely in competition; that is, their abundance is restricted by the presence of the other species but the ecological hyperspace of one does not include nor is it included in the ecological hyperspace of the other. In Case 3 the region on the graph that lies between the isocline for species N_1 and that for species N_2 represents an ecological space projected into two dimensions that can be entered by members of the species N_1 but not by species N_2; the area below the N_2 isocline is available to both species. Case 4 is the converse of Case 3.

On the basis of this very simple model, several concepts can be constructed, among which is the concept of ecological space. It is obvious that a real species or population must have some definable distribution in space and time. It is also true that a physical region occupied by any particular species is characterizable in terms of the physiology of that species. The physical space in which the population is actually found will, in general, have physical and chemical properties that encompass only a portion of the physiological tolerance limit of the species.

As previously discussed, Hutchinson (1957) has broadly outlined this concept by considering two properties of an organism— say its heat tolerance and its light tolerance—and plotting them one against the other. In this case it would be assumed that the organism lives or dies as a function of heat and light and that there is no interaction between heat and light. A rectangular space on the heat-light plane defines the viable range of heat and light for the organism. If we now were to add a third factor of the environment, say humidity, and took its coordinate at 90° to the heat-light plane we would have a boxlike space in three dimensions that is a representation of the ecological niche or ecological space of the species in question, so far as it relates to the three parameters in question. We can also add other parameters that may be significant, thereby forming an n-dimensional space that will contain all possible spaces in which the organism might be found.

Abandoning the requirement of all-or-none survival permits

construction of a "probability of survival" space in n dimensions that represents the physiological or intrinsic niche of the species in question. These regions of ordinary geometric space that actually can be characterized by a finite probability of their containing a member of the appropriate species will also meet the various physiological requirements used to define the "intrinsic" or "physiological" or "fundamental" ecological niche of the species. An ecological axiom underlying Gause's model is that no two species can indefinitely continue to occupy the same ecological niche. In other words, for any two species there exists no single region of physical space in which they both have identical survival probabilities. Operationally it seems most appropriate to define an ecological niche or ecological space as that space which no two species can continue to occupy for an indefinitely long period of time. This statement is known as the "Gause hypothesis" or, more properly, as "Gause's axiom."

In the four cases of the Gause model the physical containers involved can be classified as follows: The container utilized in Case 1 is in the intersection between the ecological niches of species N_1 and N_2. Either species can fill the entire space of this container. In Case 3 and Case 4, all of the container is within the physical manifestation of the ecological space of one of the species but is not completely within the ecological space of the other species. In Case 2, the container represents the intersection between the ecological space of both species and also includes a part of the ecological space of each species that is not included in the ecological space of the other.

The most significant point to be drawn from the model is that whereas physical parameters of ordinary geometric space change continuously and slowly, the outcome of competition between species occupying this space can be expected to be discontinuous. In other words, a discontinuous distribution of species along a continuous environmental gradient should be found in nature—and, indeed, this is the case. If, for example, you examine a rock in the tidal zone of Long Island Sound, preferably choosing one that at high tide is dry on the top, you will find that one species of barnacle is restricted to the upper portion of the rock and another species to the mid portion, and at extreme low tide you may find still a third species at the basal portion of the rock. The rock's exposure to dryness between tides is a more or less continuous function of depth, but the demarcations between the barnacle species on the rock are discontinuous. Another example is found in the fact that each of the three species of grasses usually present in saline marshes is restricted to a zone in the continual gradation of soil moisture and soil salinity. The coefficients of competition α and β are continuous functions of environmental variables; hence discontinuous zonation may be the outcome of interspecific competition.

It should be observed that in the notation of the model the two species need not be identical in all respects in order to occupy the same ecological niche. Identity of the two species would require the coefficients of competition to equal unity; identity of niche simply requires that the coefficients of competition be reciprocals of each other. For example, consider two species in a particular environment, one of which has a saturation value of $K_1 = 100$ and the other a value of $K_2 = 50$. If they utilize the environment in precisely the same way we could say that each individual of species N_2 occupies twice the ecological space of an individual of species N_1—that is, $\beta = 2$; and conversely, each individual of species N_1 occupies one half the space of an individual of species N_2—that is, $\alpha = \frac{1}{2}$. In this case, $K_2 = K_1/\alpha$ and $K_1 = K_2/\beta$, which implies coincidence of the isoclines of the two species. This has never been actually observed. In practice, such a system would be almost indistinguishable from Case 1 since random shifts along the isoclines could not be prevented.

In the system in which $\alpha = K_1/K_2$ and $\beta = K_2/K_1$, not only are the ecological requirements of the two species the same but resources are utilized in precisely the same way; for example, the same metabolic poisons are secreted by the two species. A more likely situation, however, is that the ecological requirements are the same but the metabolites produced by the two species are different. If the ecological niches of two species were completely identical, one of the two species would always be subject to invasion of its habitat by the other, with resultant elimination of one of the populations; in fact, it would be expected that only one of the two species would survive evolutionary time. We are not dealing with evolutionary time scales here, but we can note in passing that it is unlikely that at any given moment on the earth two such species would be alive simultaneously unless one were geographically isolated from the other.

Although these conclusions seem to follow from the Gause model and seem superficially in agreement with field observation, so many radical simplifying assumptions have been made in the construction of the model that it would be extremely interesting to know if more precise prediction of a particular experimental situation is possible.

chapter eight ❯❯❯❯❯ Gause's Experiments
and Their
Implications

Single-celled organisms most closely meet the assumed conditions of absence of time lags and age structure. They are also extremely convenient animals from an experimental standpoint. Gause therefore used various yeasts and protozoans in his pioneering studies of species growth and species competition. He was not the first to fit logistic curves to population data but the earlier fits of the logistic curve were made on metazoa, where the curve is applicable only to the initial portion of the population history.

These initial studies of Gause (1934), on competition between two species of yeast, are so simple and of such great historical significance we will analyze them in some detail here. His taxonomic designation of the organisms is almost certainly incorrect, but for the sake of reference to his book we will contiinue to use his terminology. Basically two species of yeast, which Gause called *Saccharomyces sp.* and *Schizosaccharomyces sp.*, were grown separately and together in a medium consisting of an extract of brewer's yeast and water with added sugar. The medium was not renewed, but growth ceased before the sugar was exhausted, apparently because of alcohol accumulation. If the medium had been renewed, obtainable saturation levels would have been expected to be considerably higher, but no formal difference would have occurred in this case. (Richards and others have shown this by experimentally changing the rate in which used medium is replaced by fresh medium.) The results of Gause's study can be summarized as follows: When the cultures were maintained in an anaerobic condition—that is, when the flasks were not shaken during population growth—it was possible to evaluate the equilibrium levels for each species and the coefficients of competition

	Saccharomyces	*Schizosaccharomyces*
r	0.21827	0.06069
K (when grown alone)	13.0	5.8
competition coefficients	$\beta = 0.439$	$\alpha = 3.15$

where the competition coefficient listed for *Saccharomyces* is the effect of *Saccharomyces* on *Schizosaccharomyces*, and vice versa. The competition coefficients as listed are mean values derived from experiments in which both species were simultaneously introduced into equal volumes of medium, and they were calculated from the following equations (Gause, 1934):

$$\alpha = \frac{K_1 - \dfrac{dN_1/dt \times K_1}{r_1 N_1} - N_1}{N_2}$$

$$\beta = \frac{K_2 - \dfrac{dN_2/dt \times K_2}{r_2 N_2} - N_2}{N_1}$$

The values of the coefficients vary with time, and Gause used the mean of three determinations.

The competition coefficients above are interpreted as "One unit of volume of *Schizosaccharomyces* decreases the unutilized opportunity for growth of *Saccharomyces* 3.15 times as much as one unit of *Saccharomyces* itself; *Saccharomyces* decreases the unutilized opportunity of growth of *Schizosaccharomyces* 0.439 times as much as one unit of *Schizosaccharomyces* itself." Gause points out that if alcohol is actually the limit to population growth in these yeasts it should be possible to evaluate directly the competition coefficients in terms of relative rates of alcohol production in the two species. From these rates the competition coefficients are computed as $\alpha' = 2.186$ and $\beta' = 1/\alpha' = 0.457$. The fact that

$\beta \approx \beta'$ implies that *Saccharomyces* only affects *Schizosaccharomyces* by the production of alcohol, but since $\alpha \neq \alpha'$ it must be concluded that *Schizosaccharomyces* produces something in addition to alcohol that alters the growth of *Saccharomyces*. An alternative interpretation is that *Schizosaccharomyces* is affected in its growth only by alcohol but some other metabolite in addition to alcohol affects the growth of *Saccharomyces*.

In repeating these experiments with aerated cultures, Gause found an alteration in the coefficients of competition: Specifically, the depressing effect of *Schizosaccharomyces* on *Saccharomyces* was reduced and the reverse effect was doubled. The parameters α and β, as determined from the population data, then coincided completely with relative rates of alcohol production. Gause therefore concluded that some respiratory by-product, presumably carbon dioxide, was involved in the anaerobic competition situation but was no longer significant under aerated conditions.

Although there is probably no major significance in the outcome of competition between two mislabeled species of yeast grown in a crude medium, it is significant that population competition theory as developed by Volterra (*cf.* D'Ancona, 1954), Gause, etc., not only can provide an empirical description of population growth under certain circumstances but can lead to a recognition and definition of physiological factors in the growth of a population. The theory can effectively translate between what has been called the physiological and population levels of integration. These experiments are also of interest in that they provide a direct demonstration of the effect of altering a system's physical environment on the outcome of biological competition in that system. In Hutchinson's notation of ecological niches, the process of shaking the cultures changed the ecological state in the culture vessel so that it became closer to the center of the ecological niche of *Saccharomyces* than it had been previously.

Gause continued his studies with combinations of competitive species, producing various of the theoretical possibilities of interspecific competition. None of these experiments could be as simply or neatly analyzed as those with the yeasts, however. He demonstrated, for example, that frequent changing of the culture medium seriously altered the pattern of competition between the protozoan species *Paramecium caudatum* and *Paramecium aurelia* since

P. caudatum was more sensitive to metabolitic accumulation than was *P. aurelia* (Gause, 1935).

In the experiments with *P. caudatum* and *P. aurelia* both species grew rapidly in the early stages of mixed population growth, essentially at the rate predicted from isolated cultures. After five days of mixed growth the rate of increase changed drastically for both species. At equilibrium in isolated cultures there were 64 *P. caudatum* per cc and 105 *P. aurelia;* that is, one *P. caudatum* occupied 1/64 of the ecological space in an equilibrium population of *P. caudatum* and one *P. aurelia* occupied 1/105 of the ecological space in a population of pure *P. aurelia*. On the fifth day in the mixed cultures there were 25 *P. caudatum* and 65 *P. aurelia*. We can translate the ecological effect of one *P. aurelia* into that of one *P. caudatum* as 64/105 = .61; inversely, the ecological effect of one *P. caudatum* expressed in units of *P. aurelia* is 1.64. A mixed culture containing 25 caudatum and 65 aurelia can be translated into units of *P. caudatum* as $25 + (0.61 \times 65) = 65$ "caudatum units," which agrees remarkably well with the already observed caudatum saturation level of 64 individuals. Correspondingly, there are 106 aurelia units at day 5 consisting of 65 aurelia plus $(1.64 \times .25)$ caudatum. From the fifth day on, the competition coefficients are paramount in determining relative volumes of both species, and both species are essentially at their saturation level. *P. caudatum* subsequently was eliminated by competition, the precise mechanism of which could not be determined.

Note that in the solution for the general conditions for the outcome of competition only the saturation values, K_1 and K_2, and the competition coefficients appear. This implies that, at least in a formal sense, the intrinsic rate of natural increase is not of significance in determining the outcome of competition in a constant environment. The ability to fill rapidly an ecological space seems to have no connection with the ability to hold that space against a competitor. Although this concept is formally statable and mathematically reasonable, its biological implications are somewhat more difficult to grasp. When two species are competing, and the environment is essentially saturated with one or both of them, the relative number of animals in the two species will change only as the normal deaths in the population are replaced differentially by members of the two species. This replacement process involves a momentary alleviation of saturation and a momentary value of R_0 in one population that is greater than the corresponding value for the other population. The value of r used in fitting the population growth equations is calculated either by fitting the curves for the condition of $N_1 = N_2 = 0$ or from $l_x m_x$ data in the manner indicated previously. In any case this calculated value is so much in excess of the degree of realization of r at or near saturation that the formal solution is concerned only with saturation values and the competition coefficients.

Since reproduction is almost certainly a significant property of a population from the standpoint of competition it is advisable to explore theoretical formulations that retain the concept r in the conditions for interspecific competitive success. Formulations of this type become mathematically difficult very quickly. One simple modification of the competition equations that has the desired effect of indicating the relative significance of r in the competition process is outlined by Gause (1935). He introduces an extremely simple rarefaction process into the two-species competition situation by assuming that organisms of both populations are being removed at a rate m. This factor can be thought of either as a nonspecific predator or as the washing away or replacement of a constant fraction of the experimental volume—for example, the overflow of a small pool in a stream.

Introducing a rarefaction into the species competition equations as the single term m, we have

$$\frac{dN_1}{dt} = r_1 N_1 \left(\frac{K_1 - N_1 - \alpha N_2}{K_1} \right) - m N_1$$

$$\frac{dN_2}{dt} = r_2 N_2 \left(\frac{K_2 - N_2 - \beta N_1}{K_1} \right) - m N_2$$

The N_2 isocline is now $N_2 = K_2 (1 - m/r_2) - \beta N_1$ and the N_1 isocline is $N_1 = K_1 (1 - m/r_1) - \alpha N_2$. The conditions for the outcome of competition corresponding to the four cases listed on page 63 are

$$\textit{Case 1:} \quad \frac{\alpha}{1 - m/r_1} > \frac{K_1/K_2}{1 - m/r_2} \quad \text{and} \quad \frac{\beta}{1 - m/r_2} > \frac{K_2/K_1}{1 - m/r_1}$$

Case 2: $\dfrac{\alpha}{1 - m/r_1} < \dfrac{K_1/K_2}{1 - m/r_2}$ and $\dfrac{\beta}{1 - m/r_2} < \dfrac{K_2/K_1}{1 - m/r_1}$

Case 3: $\dfrac{\alpha}{1 - m/r_1} < \dfrac{K_1/K_2}{1 - m/r_2}$ and $\dfrac{\beta}{1 - m/r_2} > \dfrac{K_2/K_1}{1 - m/r_1}$

Case 4: $\dfrac{\alpha}{1 - m/r_1} > \dfrac{K_1/K_2}{1 - m/r_2}$ and $\dfrac{\beta}{1 - m/r_2} < \dfrac{K_2/K_1}{1 - m/r_1}$

These involve both the rate of increase, r, and the rate of depletion, m.

The most interesting consequence of the formulation is that the outcome of competition of two species may be reversed by a nonselective predator. That is, it is possible to visualize the three-dimensional graph of N_1 versus N_2 versus m (Fig. 8-1), in which at low levels of m one species—say N_1—wins in competition whereas at somewhat higher values of m both of the species persist and at the highest value of m the other species—in this case N_2—persists alone. In such a graph the isoclines are replaced by isoplanes. For species N_1 this isoplane is defined by the three intercepts $N_1 = K_1$, $N_2 = K_1/\alpha$, and $m = b_1$. The locus of equilibrium points for persistent mixtures of the two species is defined by the line of intersection of the two planes. It should be noted, however, that if m stays constant with time, Gause's axiom still holds.

Imagine Fig. 8-1 to represent three sides of a box. The back of the box is the plane AOB, characterized by $m = 0$. The lines on this plane represent the isoclines for species N_1 and N_2 in the absence of predation or rarefaction. The floor of the box is the plane COB, characterized by $N_2 = 0$. The lines on this plane represent the interaction between m and species N_1. The side of the box is the plane COA and the lines on this plane represent the interaction between species N_2 and m. Two intersecting planes cut through the three walls of the box. One of these planes, which intersects the m, N_1, and N_2 axes at r_1, K_1, and K_1/α respectively, is the isoplane for species N_1. Any point on this plane corresponds to a set of values for m, N_1 and N_2 that will satisfy the condition $dN_1/dt = 0$. The other plane intersects the m, N_1, and N_2 axes at the points r_2, K_2/β, and K_2 respectively. This is the isoplane for species N_2 and every point on this plane satisfies the condition $dN_2/dt = 0$. The line ED represents the intersection of these two planes and at any point along this line $dN_1/dt = dN_2/dt = 0$. Points E' and D' represent the projection of points E and D respectively onto the m axis. In Fig. 8-1, for all values of m less than D' the N_1 isoplane is higher than the N_2 isoplane and species N_1 will win in competition with species N_2.

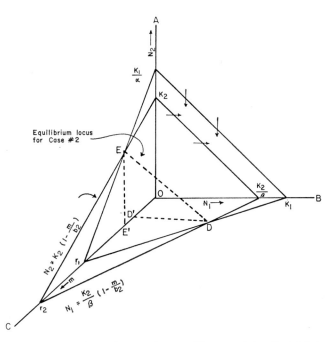

Fig. 8-1. The relation between interspecific competition, the intrinsic rate of natural increase (r) and predation, when species N_1 would win in the absence of predation but species N_2 has a higher intrinsic rate of increase.

This may be readily visualized by imagining a series of planes parallel to OAB cutting through the m axis. All such planes that cut the m axis at $m < D'$ will have the properties of Case 3, as discussed with reference to the simple competition equations. If one of these planes should be parallel to OAB and cut the m axis at some value of m such that $E' > m > D'$, then the isoclines of N_1 and N_2 on that plane would intersect at a point that will represent a stable equilibrium of the type of Case 2. Any plane parallel to the OAB plane but cutting the m axis at $m > E'$ will show isoclines in which the isocline of species N_2 is everywhere higher than that of N_1 and would correspondingly imply that species N_2 would win in competition—that is, would be an example of Case 4 of the competition equations. Any plane cutting the m axis at some point for which $m > r_1$ will represent an ecological situation that does not include the ecological niche of species N_1 at all.

This model suggests that the rate of depletion imposed by the environment is a component of the ecological niche. In Fig. 8-1, a physical space with a low removal rate favors one species; a space with a high removal rate favors the other species; and a space having an intermediate removal rate actually seems to consist of two ecological niches that only partially overlap. This would be interpreted to mean that species N_1 is adapted physiologically to the conditions in the space in question but has, in a sense, purchased this adaptation at the cost of reproductive speed; whereas species N_2, although it may not be as well adapted in one sense as species N_1, does have an adaptation to removal rate as such. In the region of stable equilibrium the relative advantages of the two species are just compensated by the removal rate m and there is actually an overlap between two ecological niches. Unless the isoclines on the plane OAB are parallel to each other there will always be a transitional zone at some intermediate value of m at which both species will persist.

As previously noted, Case 1 requires that both species inhibit each other more than they inhibit themselves. Starting with this situation, predation can alter the outcome of competition so that it is no longer independent of initial concentration but it cannot cause the two species to exist in equilibrium with each other. The effect of predation on Case 1 is illustrated in Fig. 8-2. As m increases, either line K_2,r_2 will intersect line $K_1/\alpha,r_1$ or line K_1,r_1 will intersect line $K_2/\beta,r_2$. In the former case, $m > D'$ implies that species N_1 will win in competition regardless of the initial concentrations of N_1 and N_2 (Fig. 8-2a). In the latter case, $m > D'$ implies that N_2 will win in competition regardless of the initial concentrations of N_1 and N_2 (Fig. 8-2b). If in the absence of predation species N_1 and N_2 can coexist indefinitely (Case 2), then the only possible effect of severe predation is to cause the species with the lower value of r to be eliminated (Fig. 8-3).

In brief, predation intensity of an unselective kind can alter the outcome of competition between two species in such a way that two species can continue to coexist in a space in which only one

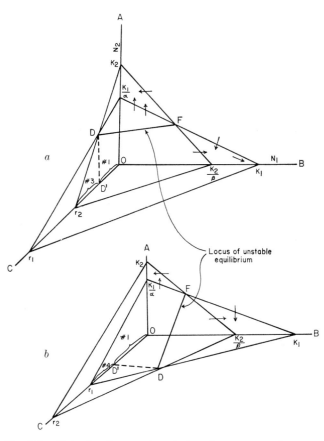

Fig. 8-2. If, in the absence of predation, the outcome of competition between two species depends on initial concentration, Case 1, then predation will favor the species with the higher intrinsic rate of increase. Axes as in Fig. 8-1.

species could exist without predation; or conversely, predation may upset an equilibrium between two species so that one species will disappear in competition. In a two-species interaction in which the outcome is dependent on initial concentrations of organisms, increased predation can eliminate the possibility of the species with the lower value of r ever winning in competition.

The above analysis is the simplest possible model that has any resemblance to reality. It is assumed here that the predation rate itself is constant, which is unrealistic in the case of a food-limited predator but is a fair approximation to the situation in which

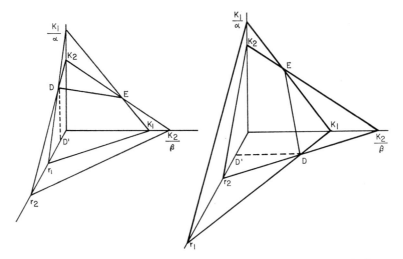

Fig. 8-3. Sufficiently heavy predation will eliminate the species with the lower value of r, even if both species can persist indefinitely in the absence of predation. Axes as in Fig. 8-1.

animals are removed from the population by some physical force. It is very unlikely that predation will operate at random on two different species, but any preference by the removal agency for one species will probably be equivalent to simply altering the relative values of r for the two species.

There are three experimental systems in which the alteration of the outcome of competition by predation or rarefaction has been observed. Park (1955) found that the outcome of competition between the flour beetles *Tribolium castaneum* and *T. confusum* usually resulted in the survival of only *T. castaneum,* but if the cultures were infected with the sporozoan parasite *Adelina tribolii,* *T. confusum* usually won in competition.

Utida (1953) experimentally demonstrated that in competition between the Azuki bean weevil (*Callosobruchus chinensis*) and the southern cowpea weevil (*C. quadrimaculatus*) the cowpea weevil loses when the two species are maintained on azuki beans. If a parasitic wasp (*Neocatolaccus mamezophagus*) is added to the mixed species cultures, both weevil species persist indefinitely. The wasp shows no preference between species. In this case there is an increase of stability as a result of adding a parasite.

In competition between a brown hydra (*Hydra littoralis*) and a green hydra (*Chlorohydra viridissima*) in the light, Slobodkin (1961) found that in the absence of predation the green hydra invariably eliminated the brown. By raising the animals in the dark or by removing a fixed percentage of the newborn animals of each species, however, the two populations were stabilized and persisted together for the duration of the experiment. In this case either a single change in a physical factor or the imposition of an extra and indiscriminate source of mortality permitted two species to persist in a space in which only one would otherwise persist. The green hydra had an extra energy source in the form of photosynthesis and had a higher reproductive rate. The energy loss to the green hydra population through predation was therefore greater than the loss to the brown, compensating for the difference in energy income. The two species are clearly in different ecological niches in this case.

More detailed description of metazoan populations will have to wait until we discuss the effect of age structure differences and time lags on the transition between logarithmically growing steady states and saturated steady states.

Various modifications can be made in the basic equations (Kostitsyn, 1937). For example, by altering the signs of the coefficients of competition we can produce first-order models for such phenomena as predation of one species on another, symbiotic interaction between species, or parasitic interaction between species. In fact, by suitable definition of terms, alteration of signs of coefficients, and perhaps the addition of one or two coefficients to the equation, we can convince ourselves that we are developing a theory of ecology while we watch the empirical ecological world slowly disappear into the limbo of natural history. Therefore, rather than expand this two-species model it is advisable to return to the initial assumptions underlying our original sigmoid growth equation for a single species.

> >
> >
> >
> >
> >

chapter nine

Weakness of the Sigmoid Growth Model; Growth of Metazoan Populations

In the sigmoid growth equation and in the subsequent species competition equations we have assumed that the degree of crowding in the population is suitably measured by a sum of the number of animals present and that there is a linear response to crowding in each animal of the population. If this is the case, it should be found that the energy input into the space in which a population is growing will add a proportionate increment to the saturation level. The proportionality constant should be related to the cost of maintenance of the saturation population.

This may be represented by

$$K' = aN$$

where K' is the energy input, a is a proportionality constant, and N is the number of animals in the population at saturation. It may be found, however, that the relation between the energy input and the number of animals in the population at saturation cannot be represented as a straight line at all, but only as a relatively complex curve—for example

$$K' = aN + bN^2 + cN^3 \cdots$$

82

Although higher order terms may be significant, only the coefficients of the first three terms seem to have biological meaning (Slobodkin, 1953a). The first-order coefficient, a, would seem to represent direct interaction between animals in their competition for food. The second-order coefficient, b, may represent alteration in the physio- logical demands or requirements of the members of a population stemming from their direct interaction with other members of the population. Mutual poisoning by metabolites, behavioral inter- actions, and other social interactions would have this effect. Where metabolite poisoning is of primary significance, a curvilinear relation between population saturation level and energy supply is expected.

It is possible to assign a biological meaning also to the third- order coefficient, c, relating to the occurrence of social subgroups that alter the physiology of each animal in the population. The effect of a neighboring band of monkeys on a single monkey of a different band might well be of this type. In general, this factor may be of significance in any animals that have a family or tribal structure. If the size of an equilibrium population of animals in which a family structure is relevant is plotted against energy inflow into the population, a maximum of N/K' may exist (Slobodkin, 1953a). In a sense, this maximum can be considered the optimal density; that is, the population is smaller per unit energy consumed at both higher and lower levels of population size than in the region of the maximum.

On purely formal grounds optimal densities are found only in populations that have the following relation to K'

$$K' = aN - bN^2 + cN^3$$

Setting $c = 1$, the possible ratio $a : b$ that will permit optimal density to occur is defined as the range that will permit N/K' to have a maximum at some value of N. Over an extremely wide range of conceivable physiological systems, optimal densities are less than 10 animals per population, ranging from $N = 2$ at $a = 3b$ to $N = 9$ at $a = 1000b$. These values are in agreement with those experi- mentally determined for Cladocera, where an optimal density of five animals per container has been found; for mice, in which an optimal density of two to four animals has been found; and for flour beetles, in which two to four animals is optimal. In the above discussion we are dealing with steady-state conditions where age structure effects that may invalidate our general model of the transition between a logarithmically growing and an equilibrium population are not significant.

Just as social interaction, as defined above, may influence the relation between a single population and its environment, it will also alter the pattern of interspecific competition (Hutchinson, 1947). Consider a situation in which the interaction between two species can be represented as

$$\frac{dN_1}{dt} = r_1 N_1 \frac{K_1 - N_1 - \gamma N_2^2}{K_1}$$

$$\frac{dN_2}{dt} = r_2 N_2 \frac{K_2 - N_2 - \delta N_1^2}{K_2}$$

where γ and δ have values of the same order of magnitude as the coefficients of linear competition discussed previously, and the isoclines for the two populations are now the second-order equations

$$\frac{dN_1}{dN_2} = 0, \ K_1 - N_1 - \gamma N_2^2 = 0$$

$$\frac{dN_2}{dN_1} = 0, \ K_2 - N_2 - \delta N_1^2 = 0$$

The isocline for N_1 cuts the N_1 axis at K_1 and the N_2 axis at $\sqrt{K_1/\gamma}$; the isocline for N_2 cuts the N_2 axis at K_2 and the N_1 axis at $\sqrt{K_2/\delta}$. This shift from nonsocial to social interaction can transform a competition situation in which one or the other species always is victorious into a situation in which competitive outcome depends on initial concentrations of the two forms. It was suggested by the competitive interaction between species of terns nesting on isolated islands, and it seems to be of empirical significance in competition between chlorella and other species of algae.

Experimental population studies permit extremely complex mathematical analysis. As a mathematical model increases in complexity, however, its applicability to generalized ecological problems correspondingly diminishes. We will therefore not pursue the complete theoretical ramifications of the experimental situations we have already discussed, but will rather discuss a single metazoan population in some detail, particularly noting the contrast between a metazoan and protozoan population and the divergence of metazoan populations in general from the mathematical theory as outlined.

Since genetic diversity, behavioral complexity, and advanced intellectual activity on the part of the experimental animals can make a theoretical analysis extremely difficult, I have, up to now, confined my work to metazoans, which are stupid and have no social organization that I can discover (in the psychological sense of the word). Sex, while present in the species, is avoidable during the terms of the experiment. The genus Daphnia, with which I have done most of my work, has extremely elementary behavioral responses to food. Food is simply suspended in the water and the animal filters it out with an anatomical filter apparatus built into its legs. I have also worked with hydra, which sit on the bottom of their container with arms outstretched waiting for food to drop into them.

The procedure in the Daphnia studies is essentially as follows. A female Daphnia is introduced into a small container of water with a measured amount of unicellular algae. At intervals of two to four days all of the animals found in the population are counted and sorted as to size, and, since the unborn eggs are carried in a transparent sac on the back of the mother, the reproductive condition of each female is checked by counting its eggs. The cultures are maintained in this way for periods of 10 months to one-and-one-half years for each experiment.

Initially, the number of eggs per female is enormous (Slobodkin, 1954a). As many as 60 eggs can be carried by a single *Daphnia obtusa* and 125 eggs by a single *Daphnia magna*. Since the eggs require only three to four days to reach hatching age, the population increases at an extremely rapid rate, with young animals constituting the overwhelming majority at this initial stage. The population continues to increase for 20 to 40 days, depending on the amount of food available. At the end of that time reproduction stops and the size distribution in the population begins to shift so that more and more large animals appear, while the total number of animals decreases. The number of eggs found in the brood pouches of the individual female decreases markedly, to as few as two eggs per 50 females. About the 75th day the population increases slightly and then decreases again. Finally, at about the 100th day of population history, almost all of the animals present are large, nonreproducing females. There is again an increase in population, sometimes with a shift in size distribution toward young animals, but this new

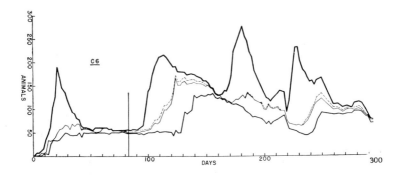

Fig. 9-1. *Above,* Daphnia population growth curve. Adult animals are indicated by the height of the lowest line, adolescent animals and young are superimposed on the adults. The number of adolescents is the difference between the lowest curve and the second curve. The total population size is indicated by the top curve. The vertical line at day 82 indicates a 3-degree temperature drop. This population stayed essentially constant from day 40 to day 90. *Below,* a second Daphnia population growth curve, using the same system of presentation as above. This population never stayed constant. (From Slobodkin, 1954a.)

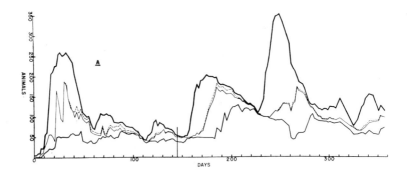

population peak is much lower than the initial one. The population will then either continue to show slight fluctuations, with an almost completely adult population at a low point and the greatest frequency of young animals at the high points; or the population will develop a stable size distribution. In this distribution there are

some representatives of all size categories, but there is a preponder-
ance of nonreproducing adults. The number of animals in the
population then stays constant.

If the number of animals in a stable population is plotted
against food supply, a completely linear relation between population size and food level is found. If a set of fluctuating populations
that do not show a particularly convincing linearity with food
supply are killed and the complete animals analyzed for total
nitrogen content, a linearity with food supply is found, regardless
of the lack of correspondence between food supply and the *number*
of animals.

It is clear from our early analysis that there cannot be any
social interaction between the animals in the population and hence
all existing interactions must be mediated through the food supply.
It was incidentally determined by microscopic examination of culture water that all the algae provided as food are removed from
all populations 10 hours after feeding and that in the remainder
of the time between feedings the population consequently has
no food at all.

The mechanism of population growth can be reconstructed
from this information. The presence of any animal in the population lowers the amount of food that will be acquired by all the
other animals in the population. Since growth and reproduction
are both dependent on food, the growth rate and reproductive
rate of competing animals are reduced. Eventually starvation becomes so severe that the production of new eggs ceases, although the
eggs already in the brood chambers of their mothers will continue
to develop and give rise to normal, healthy, small animals. (The
embryos do not depend on the mother for nutrient once the egg
has been extruded from the oviduct.) The birth of these young
will cause a further increase in the severity of starvation, a
further decrease in the growth rate, and a slight increase in
the probability of death in the population. The death of any
animal in the population, at this point, releases a slightly greater
food ration for the survivors. The initial effect of this increased food
ration is to cut the death rate. Any food available to the individual
animals above the minimum subsistence requirements is first
utilized for growth, but increase in the size of the surviving animals
also increases their capacity to remove food from the water, since

the filtering rate is proportional to the size of the individual animals. An increase in size of the survivors will also increase the total amount of protoplasm that must be supported by the available food, so that the starvation of the animals will not be greatly alleviated and it will be impossible for reproduction to start again. The number of animals in the population will therefore continue to decline at the same time as the size distribution shifts toward large animals and starvation continues. The minor secondary peak in population size seems to occur when the first young that are born into the population finally mature and reproduce. Finally, adult females are the only survivors.

Daphnia, like most animals, have a lower growth rate after they reach reproductive maturity than they do earlier in their life. Therefore, when the population is composed completely of reproductive-size females any deaths that occur in the population will result in an increased reproduction rate among the survivors. A new crop of newborn is therefore produced, which inhibits further reproduction on the part of their mothers. A situation of starvation ensues, followed either by a repetition of the same process or by attainment of stable age distribution.

The bases of the fluctuations in the population are the various temporal lags in the adjustment of the population to its food supply. The stable age distribution is one in which these lags are minimized. The significant time lag phenomena in Daphnia populations are:

(1) An approximately four- to six-day lag in the effect of changed food conditions on the reproductive rate of any one animal. This is the time between extrusion of the egg into the brood chamber and release of the young from the brood chamber.

(2) A time lag in the effect of the newborn animal on the food supply of the other animals in the population due to the change in size and feeding capacity as the newborn animal grows. Growth time from birth to reproductive maturity varies in Daphnia from approximately five days to approximately 40 days, depending on temperature and food supply.

(3) A complex time lag in the adjustment of the age structure of the population to any initial distortion from the stable age structure. This varies with the initial distortion and may be as long as three or four generations.

If the population consists completely of adults living at a bare survival food level, the death of one adult releases new food, resulting in the production of a young animal and in a distortion of the size frequency distribution of the population. If we imagine the birth of one young to replace an adult that has died, we can consider that the food ration is still slightly in excess of survival requirements, since the young animal does not have the feeding capacity of the adult being replaced. Therefore, we can expect that new young will be produced while the initial replacement animal is growing up. In short, fluctuations in numbers of animals occur that are completely independent of the environment.

Given a population in which the distribution of sizes of animals is such that the excess food released by the death of the oldest animal will permit one animal to produce one newborn and permit all of the survivors to grow just enough to re-establish the initial size distribution and starvation level, then the population will have readjusted to the death of the original adult in a minimum of time. On both theoretical and experimental grounds it is clear that the size distribution of this population is such that the frequency of animals in any size category is inversely proportional to the growth rate of an animal in that size category. It can be shown as a theorem that the growth pattern of animals born into this population is constant, that the age at which reproduction occurs is either constant or has a constant time distribution, and that the probability of death at any age is constant. The growth rate of animals of the same age is also constant from time to time.

In a stochastic model there will be a fixed size distribution of animals of any age and this distribution will be constant at equilibrium. In Daphnia it has been shown experimentally that neither age alone nor size alone is a sufficient criterion for defining the future behavior of an animal in a population.

The mechanic a of Daphnia population growth outlined above was largely deduced from the shape of the population growth curves and the relation between population size and food level. The various assumptions have been handsomely analyzed experimentally by Frank and his co-workers (Frank, Boll, and Kelly, 1957). They first determined the survivorship and fecundity curves for *Daphnia pulex* at various levels of crowding and from this calculated the effect of crowding on r. They found r generally to be a linear function of crowding; this is also implicit in the logistic equation presented previously. In subsequent work (Frank, 1960) the degree of crowding of cohorts of animals was experimentally changed during the animals' lifetime. In general, after the crowding level had been changed, the survival and fecundity rates appropriate to the new crowding level were assumed. The survivorship rates changed immediately, but fecundity—that is, m_x values —remained intermediate between those of the two crowding levels for a period of approximately five days. Animals that were changed from a high density to a lower one seemed to show a slightly higher m_x value at the lower crowding level than animals raised at that low crowding level since birth. The total volume of an animal of a given age was greater at low crowding levels than at high crowding levels. A change in the degree of crowding resulted in alteration of the volume-age curve of the animals, but they never reached the same volume as animals of the same age that had been maintained since birth at the lower crowding level.

A result of this study was a series of tables of population data that could be combined in various ways to produce mathematical models of population growth curves. Frank considered models arranged in order of increasing complexity. The simplest of these is the logistic equation, which requires only values of r and of K, taken as the population density for which $r = 0$ (A in Fig. 9-2). The next most complex model is one in which age specific fertility and fecundity values at each numerical density are used instead of merely r and K. The prediction is very similar to that of the logistic curve. The assumptions of instantaneous response of fecundity to population density are maintained in the model (B in Fig. 9-2).

Frank then replaced the assumption of instantaneous response to population density with the assumption that the density existing five days previously controls the present fecundity. This assumption is consonant with the observed effect in his experimental determination of the effect on m_x of changing density. The predictions on this model, using either numerical density (C in Fig. 9-2) or volume density (C′ in the figure), are highly oscillatory, but the oscillations tend to damp somewhat as the populations grow older. As a final possible model, Frank considered that used by Ricker (1954) in analyzing the Daphnia population data of Pratt (1943). Ricker assumed that the number of animals alive at any given generation is determined by the density of the previous generation. In order to make this calculation Frank solved for generation time, T, at the various densities from the appropriate $l_x m_x$ data by the formula $e^{rT} = \sum l_x m_x$.

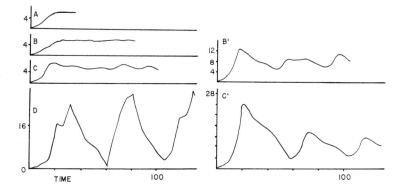

Fig. 9-2. Various theoretical curves for the growth of a Daphnia population. (Unpublished material printed with the kind permission of Dr. Peter Frank.) Curve and theoretical assumptions are as follows: Curve A: r and K are sufficient for the prediction of population growth. B: Age specific birth rates are significant. These respond instantaneously to numerical population density. B': Age specific birth and death rates are determined instantaneously by population volume. C: Age specific birth and death rates are determined by the number of animals five days previously. C': Age specific birth and death rates are determined by the total volume of the population five days previously. D: Population size is determined by the population size one generation earlier.

Having constructed six predictive models, Frank then grew several *Daphnia pulex* populations and found that the observed population growth pattern was unequivocally most similar to that predicted by the model that assumed a time lag in the effect of density on births, and age and size-specific reproductive and growth rates, and also assumed total population density to be proportional to population volume rather than to population number (C').

In short, Frank explicitly tested the various inferences that had been made from growth data alone and found a generally good agreement with Daphnia population growth. It is not surprising that the model that utilized the most information about the populations also gave the closest fit to the population data. It is, however, significant that the precision of the experimental and analytic procedures is high enough to warrant the complexity of the model. In most field censusing programs it would be impossible even to attempt to distinguish between the predictive powers of these various models. The apparent lack of significant difference between the closeness of fit of field data to the various models is probably due to sampling error in the field; Frank's work indicates the necessity of attempting to construct alternative models rather than being satisfied with a plausible-sounding model that gives a poor but not impossible fit to the observed data.

The studies on Daphnia, despite the relative simplicity of the organisms and their lack of sexuality and social behavior, indicate that population growth in metazoans is a more complex problem than in Protista. It is particularly remarkable that the Daphnia populations fluctuate as a result of internal processes even in the absence of environmental reinforcement of the oscillation pattern.

Occasionally, laboratory populations tend to show even more dramatic and violent fluctuations. Perhaps the most violent internally caused (or intrinsic) fluctuations that have been experimentally discovered are those reported by Nicholson for populations of the sheep blowfly *Lucilia cuprina*. In blowflies, as in most Diptera, an individual egg is extremely small compared with the size of an adult female, and if a female reproduces at all she will produce a large number of eggs in a fairly short time. Lucilia requires primarily water and sugar for survival as an adult; however, a small but definite amount of protein food must be ingested by a female before she can reproduce. This protein meal is not universally required among Diptera and may not even be necessary for all genetic strains of Lucilia, but it is of major significance in Nicholson's experiments. The blowfly maggots feed on meat, grow to a sufficiently large size, pupate, and then emerge as adults. The size of the larva at pupation is somewhat variable, as indicated by the fact that flies emerging from small pupae may be one eighth the size of flies emerging from large pupae (Nicholson, 1957). If the larvae are starved, they grow to approximately the proper size for pupation but are unable to pupate and simply die. If an enormous number of eggs are placed on a small bit of meat, all of the larvae hatch, feed, and exhaust the meat before any of them has reached a size that will permit successful pupation.

Nicholson has experimentally determined the relation between the number of adult flies and the number of adult progeny emerging from a one-gram piece of homogenized beef brain. A careful examination of this relation (Fig. 9-3) shows that blowfly populations will oscillate strongly even when in a constant environment. Consider, for example, that 100 larvae hatch on the meat and from these 100 larvae four adult flies emerge. If these four flies produce 25 young larvae apiece, there will again be 100 larvae and no

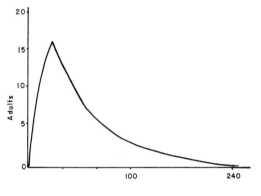

Young Larvae

Fig. 9-3. The relation between the number of larvae and the number of adults that will develop from them in experimental populations of *Lucilia cuprima*. (Redrawn from Nicholson, 1950.)

oscillation will have occurred. This system is completely unstable, as can be seen by assuming that 25 larvae are produced from every adult but that we start with 80 larvae instead of 100. From these 80 larvae five adults would emerge, producing in the next generation 125 larvae from which approximately two adults would emerge, producing 50 larvae from which 10 adults would emerge, producing 250 larvae from which no adults would emerge. The same pattern will result from any starting point on the graph.

So long as the reproductive rate is such that the surviving adults just replace the initial number of larvae, the number of adults in successive generations will stay constant; if, however, we hold the reproductive rate more or less constant, the observed relation between larvae produced and adult survival will make the equilibrium point unstable and will result in the generation of oscillations. If the reproductive rate is sufficiently low, so that the stable point for the population lies on the ascending portion of the curve, the population will return to equilibrium when displaced.

Assuming, for example, a reproductive power per adult fly of 1.5 and the same arbitrary starting point of 100 larvae, four adults will be produced that in turn will produce six larvae, resulting in approximately five adults that in turn will produce approximately seven new larvae, and so on until the population will stabilize at approximately 14 adults. Since the reproductive rate of Lucilia is much higher than this, however, the stable condition cannot be realized, at least not under circumstances in which the eggs laid during each day are kept on separate pieces of meat.

The oscillations expected on the basis of the reproductive curve can be demonstrated under a variety of circumstances. When no restriction was placed on adult food supply but the quantity of meat available to the larvae each day was restricted, the adult fly population oscillated strongly with a periodicity of approximately three weeks. The sequence of events was what would have been predicted from the experiments on larval survival and the known high adult fecundity. In Nicholson's words,

> When the numbers of adults were high such vast numbers of eggs were laid that all of the food provided was consumed while the larvae were still too small to pupate. Consequently, no adult offspring resulted from eggs laid during such periods. The adult numbers therefore dwindled progressively, until a point was reached at which the intensity of larval competition became so reduced that some of the larvae attained a sufficient size to pupate. These gave rise to egg-laying adults after a developmental period of about two weeks. In the meantime the population continued to dwindle, thus further reducing the intensity of larval competition, and permitting increasing numbers of larvae to pupate and to produce adults eventually. Consequently, for about two weeks after the appearance of the first adults of this new generation, more adults continued to emerge. This caused the adult population to rise again to a high level at which too many eggs were laid to permit larval survival, so completing a cycle (Nicholson, 1957, p. 156).

Despite the violent fluctuations of adult numbers, the mean

number of adults in these experiments was doubled when the food ration per day given to the larvae was doubled. The amplitude of the fluctuations in adult numbers could be damped only by experimental designs in which adult nutrition was also limited, by restriction in protein, sugar, or water. An analogy can be drawn between the oscillation system in blowflies and the oscillations in temperature that would occur in a room in which the thermostat is on one side of a partition and the heater on another. When the region around the thermostat becomes cold, the heat is turned on on the other side of the partition. Only after the heated portion becomes hot enough to warm the partition is the thermostat affected by the heat; and at that time the heated side of the partition is much warmer than indicated on the thermostat setting. Similarly, not until two weeks after the number of adults is so great that larval survival is either severely reduced or completely impossible does the number of adults in the population stop increasing. By this time the number of adults is well above the mean number that can be supported by the combined larval and adult environment. In the absence of limited nutrition for the adults the only control mechanism available to the population is alteration in larval survival. When limitations are imposed on the adult world the subsidiary control mechanism of alteration in adult fecundity also comes into play.

In the Daphnia populations all the animals interact with each other in competing for the available food supply immediately. In the blowfly population, however, the ecological difference between a maggot, pupa, and adult makes direct interaction between all of the animals almost impossible, and hence time lags in response to population density are almost irreducible. Nicholson's experimental technique enhances the time lags, since there is no possible interaction between larvae born on different pieces of meat. It is conceivable that if the larvae of different ages were free to interact with each other the periodicity of successful hatching would be less marked and the fluctuations in adults would have lower amplitude, even without a limitation on the adult population.

If the larvae are given unlimited food while the adults are restricted, the oscillations in adult population size are just as severe as they are when only the larvae are limited. In this case only a few adults are able to achieve a sufficiently high nutritional level to reproduce. Despite the lack of naturalness in Nicholson's experiments and the possibility that the violent population fluctuations might be eliminated by suitable experimental design, the populations show strong relatively regular fluctuations that do not correspond to any known fluctuation in the environment. The environment in these experiments is very carefully controlled and there is very little likelihood that anything other than the internal mechanism of overcrowding already discussed is significant in causing the population fluctuations.

Nicholson succeeded in imposing fluctuations on Lucilia populations by means of periodically altering the adult food supply. Nicholson reports that, in general, the populations eventually took on the same periodicity as the fluctuating food supply or some simple fraction of this periodicity. In a constant environment the populations fluctuated with their own periodicity, but in a fluctuating environment the populations generally fluctuated at the periodicity imposed by the environment.

The Daphnia represent a situation in which all the individuals of the population interact with each other and each individual changes its physiological properties as a result of population growth. The blowfly experiments, however, involve animals that do not interact together, and the main brunt of physiological adjustment is felt by only one group in the population. Some of the grain insect experiments represent a somewhat different situation, in which social interaction of a peculiar kind occurs between individuals and is equally significant with physiological change in controlling population size.

A monumental series of studies on the population dynamics of flour beetles has been made by Park (1955) and his co-workers at the University of Chicago. Summarizing the population growth pattern of these animals considerably oversimplifies some very careful and complex work, but a condensation of the results is necessary here, since an adequate report on the work would be longer than this entire book. The experimental situation in the flour beetle populations consists of sifted, humidified, temperature-equilibrated flour mixed with brewer's yeast, placed in vials or bottles of various sizes. A few beetle imagoes are introduced. Egg laying and burrowing through the flour start almost immediately, and tunnels appear in the flour. Eggs are laid in the tunnels. These eggs hatch into larvae in 5 to 10 days and the larvae and adults burrow through the flour, usually sticking to the tunnels but occasionally branching off into undisturbed flour more or less at random. The tendency to seek undisturbed flour seems to increase as the medium becomes altered—that is, conditioned—by the activities of the beetles. An egg or a pupa encountered by an adult or a larva is eaten. A certain percentage of encounters between adults of opposite sex results in copulation, which increases the production of eggs per female. Conditioning of the flour somewhat reduces fecundity per female, rate of larval development, and size of emerging imagoes. The population tends to increase through the reproduction of each female and through repeated copulations. All other interactions between the organisms tend to decrease population size. The primary interactions that decrease population size are cannibalism of eggs and pupae and the conditioning of the flour.

The typical early population history involves the production of a large number of eggs by the initial females, most of which hatch into larvae. As soon as the initial larvae have hatched and the flour has been fairly well tunnelled, egg survival becomes greatly reduced by cannibalism. The initial adults continue to lay eggs and to diminish in numbers; typically, they die either before or immediately after the emergence of the first adult females from eggs laid in the culture. These new young animals have very high fecundity but almost equally high cannibalism, and the population equilibrates with adults representing from 20 percent to 60 percent of the total numerical population, varying with species and environmental conditions. Equilibrium egg mortality through cannibalism is of the order of 90 percent or higher. In the confused flour beetle, *Tribolium confusum,* the population growth pattern is a relatively smooth increase to equilibrium. In *T. castaneum,* in which *r* is considerably higher than in *T. confusum*— at least in the absence of parasites—the population history is characterized by continual and repeated oscillations and constancy of numbers is not achieved.

Comparing the flour beetles with the blowfly and Daphnia populations, the chief control mechanism on the flour beetle is not the availability of food, but rather the density of organisms per unit volume of medium. This control is exercised not only through the activities of one stage in the life history, as it is in the blowfly, but through both the larval and adult stages, which between them constitute by far the longest portion of the life history. The control is expressed by increased mortality of two stages of the life history that are separated fairly widely from each other—namely, the defenseless states of eggs and pupae. In Daphnia populations the control on population size is exercised primarily through alteration in reproductive rates and growth rates. Once a young daphnid is born into the population its existence is no longer under the immediate control of the other animals in the population except through competition for food. In the blowfly population a young maggot, once it has hatched from the egg, is completely independent of the number of adults present in the population and its continued existence depends on its competition with only a subgroup of the population. The newborn flour beetle eggs, on the other hand, will be eliminated from the population in the egg stage as a function of the density of feeding-stage individuals; and even after they have hatched into larvae they will again be subject to control of their mortality rate as a function of the population density when they arrive at the defenseless pupa stage. The beetle populations, therefore, have several sources of population stability that are not available to the Daphnia or the blowflies. In general, the beetle populations show less fluctuation in time than the Daphnia and are certainly more stable than blowflies.

All the above cases involve mortal animals. In a study by Armstrong (1960) of the population dynamics of the flatworm *Dugesia tigrina* the animals were effectively immortal except immediately after reproduction. The animals reproduce by budding off a tail from the posterior end, which then develops its own feeding and sensory apparatus. Immediately after budding there is an open spot in the skin at the posterior end of the parent and at the anterior end of the newborn. Cannibalism by other animals in the population may eliminate these wounded animals, but this does not happen often. Aside from the possibilities of cannibalism and occasional accidental wounding during handling, each animal seems to be immortal; at least there was no sign of aging or deterioration of individuals in the six months of the study.

The number of animals in the equilibrium population varied with the pattern of approach to equilibrium. These populations either approached equilibrium from a lower level or were placed by experimental manipulation in a situation of numerical excess of organisms. The mechanism of adjustment in this case was the size of the individual animals. The total biomass of the populations at equilibrium was effectively constant per unit food supply, although some populations might consist of many small animals as opposed to those consisting of few large animals. Reproduction in these populations occurred only under conditions of environmental change.

We could continue to offer examples of single species population growth patterns, but we would find that although the detailed patterns differ, the general concepts remain quite similar up to the highly social animals in which populations and groups of animals take on the attributes of culture and historical development. As we will see later, the history of such populations may bear the imprint of the "personality" of individual animals for periods that are considerably longer than the life of these individuals.

The kinds of population growth patterns we have been discussing above are determined by the interaction between the physiological properties of the individuals, the interactions between individuals, and the physical, biological, and mechanical properties of their environment. For any particular species and environment the population growth patterns are experimentally repeatable to a surprising degree, although without detailed physiological information they may not be predictable a priori. The interactions between animals generally tend to damp the enormous increase potential available to animals in an empty environment. The effectiveness of this damping varies from species to species, and, as we will see below, the population growth pattern in the sealed, controlled environment of the laboratory has a very definite relation to the normal selective pressures operating on the species in nature.

So far we have been primarily concerned with the interaction between animals rather than with the effect of the physical environment on the populations. In general, the non-population part of the animals' environment will determine the level of population equilibrium or the level around which the population will fluctuate. It may also alter the strength of the various control interactions, but it will not qualitatively change the control mechanisms; nor can the population size be controlled in any persistent way except through modifications in the physiology, behavior, and interactions of the organisms in the population. These alterations, in general, operate as feedback devices. When a change occurs in the immediate environment of the individual animal, as a result of the activities of the other animals in the population, it is some way "sensed." "Sensed" in this case does not necessarily have anything to do with the usual conception of sense organs. It may be a biochemical sensing of the presence of other organisms through low blood sugar caused by starvation, for example. I used the term "sensed" because this change, whatever it may be, somehow activates the feedback process in the same way that—to use again the simile—deviation between the ambient temperature and the initial setting activates the relays in a thermostat to turn heat on or off.

If the population is so small or the environment so salubrious that reproductive, growth, and mortality processes can occur at a rate greater than that required for maintenance and replacement, the population will increase. If, however, the population has become excessively large, or if the environment has in some way deteriorated, the various processes that would lead to population increase may slow down while the catabolic processes will maintain their initial rate or may accelerate. In either case the effect is to diminish the population size.

The initial sensing of the deviation between the ambient environment at any given time and the environment at equilibrium may be responded to with a shorter or longer time lag and at a greater or lesser rate. The longer the time lag in the response, the greater the period and amplitude of expected oscillation in the system. The greater the immediate response, the less likely the population is to maintain relative constancy of size. In certain cases the feedback mechanisms may become highly simplified, as, for example, in the beetle populations. There, cannibalism is proportional to the number of contacts between feeding and fed-upon individuals, and the number of eggs laid is proportional to the number of females (ignoring conditioning and temperature of the medium and other secondary effects for the moment). Under these conditions the population is maintained at an approximately constant level by two forces, one of which tends to nullify the other at some unique population density. The situation is somewhat analogous to the temperature distribution in a block of metal heated from the center and exposed to an infinite capacity-low temperature bath on the outside. After an initial adjustment period, the process of heat input will just compensate for heat loss and each point in the block will assume some fixed temperature.

Nicholson (1954) has summarized the relation between the role of the environment and the role of the population itself in maintaining the population within fixed bounds. He considers that the environment of any particular population can be thought to be made up of a variety of factors, similar to the parameters of the ecological niche that we discussed previously. The relation of these various environmental factors to the population differ. Some factors cannot in any way be influenced by the population itself—at least, not to any measurable extent. Gross climatic properties or astronomical events like the normal time periodicity of a day are of this type, which he refers to as unresponsive factors. Other environmental variables can be influenced by the population itself. Microclimate or food concentration may be of this sort for some, but not necessarily all, populations. Factors of this type he calls responsive factors. If the alteration in the responsive factor in turn produces an alteration in the level of the population, Nicholson terms the responsive factor or responsive requisite as reactive and "density governing"; if the alteration produced by the population does not produce an alteration in the population level itself, the factor is referred to as nonreactive and its relation to the population is said to be "density legislative." For example, if the food supply limits a population, then the feeding of the population may reduce the food supply to the point where the population itself is reduced by starvation. Food in this case would be a responsive, reactive, density-governing factor. If, however, the food supply is not limiting—rather, the population is limited by space or predation or some other environmental variable—and if the population does not deplete the food supply sufficiently to alter the population level, then food supply would be considered as a responsive, nonreactive, and density-legislative factor. This purely terminological discussion has been introduced only to show that it is not necessarily the case that any one factor of the environment is always density governing or density dependent or density independent even with a single population of organisms, nor is it the case that any particular species need be always limited by the same environmental variables in the same way. There is a polemical literature on this subject that is not particularly fruitful in anything but verbiage and tends to obscure real problems. Although the terminology of Nicholson will not be extensively used in what follows, its introduction may save the reader from confusion when he pursues the literature further.

All of the metazoan examples we have discussed above differ from each other, but none of them can be considered to approximate the logistic curve in their growth pattern except in a very crude way. Although all of them will have an approximately sigmoid initial expansion into a new environment, none of them meet the assumptions of interchangeability between organisms and instantaneous response to environmental change that are required by the logistic equation. Each may nevertheless be described, in a meaningful and explicit way, by saying that they would meet the logistic equation conditions except for the fact that certain relevant assumptions are invalid to certain specifiable degrees. For any one of the above populations it should be possible, in principle, to construct a set of mathematical assumptions that will define the physiological properties of the organisms concerned and their interactions. Given such a set of assumptions it is possible, knowing the properties of the environment, to predict the pattern of population growth that would be followed by the species in question. We gave the example of Frank (1960) but we might have chosen the work of Neyman (Neyman et al., 1958) or Stanley (1949) or of several others who have constructed either deterministic, or in the case of Neyman, statistical models of population growth from known biological data.

There are organisms, however, in which, although the mean level attainable by a population is predictable in terms of information on the environmental and physiological level, neither the precise history of any one population nor the equilibrium level can be predicted without psychological analysis. To take a specific case, Southwick (1955) maintained six experimental populations of house mice in 25-by-6-foot pens. Three of the pens had food, water, and nest boxes distributed throughout the pen; in the • other three the food and water were in large dishes at one end and the nest boxes were crowded together at the other end. Food and water were unlimited. All six populations were followed through their initial growth, although not for a long enough time to permit any statements about population stability at equilibrium. It was clear, however, that there were enormous differences between individual populations that seemed to have no connection at all with the distribution of the food pans or nest boxes. The average of the maximum number of mice in the pens with concentrated food was identical with that in the pens in which the food pans and nest boxes were dispersed. The lowest population maximum (25) was in a dispersed pen and the highest (138) was in a concentrated pen but both situations were very variable. Southwick attributed the differences between his individual populations to temperamental differences between the animals initially introduced.

In three of his populations the primary mechanism of limiting population growth was increased mortality of the newborn litters. One population showed a decline in birth rate, combined with high litter mortality and much fighting between adults, with consequent scabbiness and mite infestation of the males. In this population ovulation and spermatogenesis were occurring at a singularly high rate. In the population that reached only 25 animals there was fighting and breaking down of nests almost from the beginning of the population's history, with attendant desertion of litters by the females. The source of the discord seems to have been the initial males. Apparently, the trampling of other animals over the females' nests led to cannibalism of the litters and generally upset the relation between the female and her offspring.

Although food was unlimited, the food consumption per mouse decreased below the minimum required to maintain normal fecundity in several of the populations. This seems to have been caused by the presence in these populations of two or more despotic males that prevented the other animals from reaching the food. Food consumption was generally higher in the populations that were sociably unstable and in which no clear despotism was established. In the unstable, high-food-consumption populations the birth rates per female were low, although the fecundity of both males and females was unimpaired. Southwick considers the possibility that this was due either to interference with normal copulation by other members of the population or to high abortion rates.

Strecker and Emlen (1953), maintaining house mouse populations in pens on limited food, found a population increase up to the time at which no excess food was available. In one population, started with 50 initial mice, a cessation of reproduction occurred at a population peak of 100 animals and the population declined slowly throughout the duration of the experiment with no new litters being produced. The study was reported for a 10-month period but in this population all the litters were born in June, July, and August. In a population started with 10 animals the population achieved a peak of only 40 animals and litters continued to be produced throughout the study. In this population there was always excess food although the total amount provided was the same as that given to the population in which reproduction ceased.

Calhoun (1952) found in a confined population of Norway rats (*Rattus norvegicus*) that population size was limited by space in conditions of unlimited food. The pen was divided by familylike groups of rats into defended territories with pathways between them leading to the central food hopper. The chief sources of mortality were apparently infection and complication of wounds initially acquired in fights between individuals.

An extremely elegant study demonstrating the occurrence of culturally determined factors in population growth and control of population structure by the personalities of the animals is that by King (1955) on the black-tailed prairie dog (*Cynomys ludovicianus*) in Shirttail Canyon in Wind Cave National Park, South Dakota. This study was made in the field. Because of the restricted nature of the terrain and the relative permanence of the various animals and constructions that make up a prairie dog town, King could examine a more or less completely closed population unit. He found that the prairie dog town was divided by natural boundaries into sections, which he called wards. By watching the movements of individual prairie dogs it became apparent that an individual prairie dog fed and traveled only in a limited subarea of the ward. King referred to these subareas and the prairie dogs that occupied them as coteries. Animals belonging to the same coterie kissed on meeting, groomed each other, and gave every evidence of enjoying each other's company. An animal outside its own coterie territory, however, seemed furtive and frightened and did not respond in kind to the various ritual friendship movements made by the residents of the coterie but either ran or fought when approached. All the individual members of a coterie seemed to learn its boundaries by watching other animals. The coterie territory was usually less than one acre, and was not always identical with the territory of an individual male. The average number of animals was eight and one-half in the coteries studied, although the range was from two to 39. Usually only four or five of these individuals were breeding animals and usually only one of these was a male. Not all of the coteries bred. Nonbreeding coteries had various sex ratios or were all of one sex. Members of a coterie generally did not leave it, but occasionally yearling animals or adults left either to join another coterie, to attempt to enlarge the boundaries of their own coterie, or to start a new set of burrows that would extend the town at its borders. A male prairie dog with what we might call a Napoleonic personality can alter the boundaries of a coterie and these boundaries will remain fixed long after he and perhaps all of his descendants have departed. He will thereby have made a permanent cultural contribution to the society. The young animals that stay behind tend to remain within the original borders of their coterie.

The remarkable point in this study is that individual animals in the coteries must not only acquire food and other requisites to survive and breed but must also assume a clear social role. This role not only refers to immediate companions but has a cultural or historical foundation in that the boundaries of the coterie territory are more constant than the personnel of the coterie.

Although the prairie dog town was too large to permit detailed population analysis, it seems possible to infer from King's work that the total effectiveness of breeding in the entire town was more dependent on the personality and behavior of the dominant males in the various coteries than on the number and physiology of the females or even on the relatively minor alterations that might occur in the physical environment.

All animals that have clear territorial restrictions or a definite pattern of restricting their spatial behavior with reference to a territory may have their population growth pattern determined to a large extent by the behavior of individuals. The mean population size and the mean fecundity and mortality rates are presumably legislated, in the sense of Nicholson, by the environment; but the variance around any predicted mean may be expected to be much greater than that anticipated in behaviorally more stereotyped animals. Individual animals belonging to species that tend to wander over a large area are less likely to develop personal behavioral idiosyncrasies that will seriously alter the mean size of the populations to which they belong. I would suspect that two herds of buffalo are more likely to have similar social patterns than are two closed pens of house mice or two coteries of prairie dogs. A bully can alter a neighborhood but he is not usually effective in a completely transient group.

chapter ten ► Escape in Time and Space

So far we have, with minor exceptions, been concerned with populations growing in sealed containers. If the development of single populations is as complex as has been indicated, even without discussing two-species systems and with almost no reference to the natural world, it may seem surprising that populations of animals actually do survive. There must be times when a combination of internal and external pressures might make it highly desirable for a population to leave some particular environment and try its luck elsewhere. Many animals have some pattern of nonseasonal migration built into their physiology in such a way that they move when, or even before, the environment in which they find themselves deteriorates or is used up.

The process of sexual reproduction itself is essentially a way of changing the relation between animals and their environment—an escape mechanism in more than a psychoanalytic sense. Almost all organisms examined have been shown to have some sort of sexual reproductive process. In fact, the burden of proof is now on those who would deny the existence of sexuality in any particular case. Aside from its other interesting features sex results in offspring that have a different complex of genetic determinants than did either of the parents alone. In some cases these determinants place the offspring in a better position than its parents for coping with its environment. In most cases, however, at least in a constant environment, the new genetic complex is less advantageous

107

than the old; parents, after all, have already demonstrated their success by living long enough to reproduce. If the environment is changing, there is no guarantee that the future world will be at all similar to the world to which the parents so successfully adapted or that the parents' genotypic endowment will be suitable for that future world. Most of the offspring will be as ill suited to the new world as to the old, but the process of sexual reproduction must occur in order to permit a selective process consonant with the new ecological conditions.

In many organisms, sexual intercourse is a permanently necessary prerequisite to reproduction. In others—some of the protozoans, for example—sex and reproduction may be separated in time. In these animals the function of sex as a reshuffler of genetic potentialities rather than a stimulus to reproduction is seen clearly. For most of the individual organisms now alive on the earth sex is a sometime thing. Daphnia are parthenogenic during the periods of rapid population increase, although males always seem to be present in low numbers. As the population becomes more crowded the egg production per female decreases and, while the population is just beginning to decelerate its numerical increase, the females are producing approximately two eggs per brood. At that time winter eggs are produced, which require fertilization. These eggs are surrounded by a protective sheath of maternal carapace, the ephippium. Ephippial—also called sexual or winter—eggs sometimes hatch after one or two days into normal-looking young. Usually, however, winter eggs do not hatch until they have been either frozen or dried. Many Daphnia populations in nature pass the nutrient-poor summer and the frozen winter in the form of winter eggs. The winter egg, therefore, acts as an escape mechanism for the Daphnia population in two ways. It is genetically new and it permits the population to escape through time from the stresses of the instant.

Generally in Diptera, the fully grown maggot emerges from the medium in which early development has taken place, pupates, and then enters a winged phase in which sexual reproduction occurs. The adult fly is a device for genetic interchange and for mobility. Blow-flies in nature do not, in all probability, have the same type of internally controlled fluctuations as are found in the laboratory, since the adult animals disperse widely instead of overloading the same bit of meat with their oviposition. In the fungus fly, *Oligarces paradoxus,* Ulrich (1940) has shown that given abundant, fresh fungal food, reproduction is paedogenetic and parthenogenic. The larvae develop ovaries without fertilization and the ovaries develop into larvae in the mother's body and emerge, killing the mother in the process. As the food supply deteriorates in quality or quantity, the number of eggs that develop in each larva decreases. When the number of eggs developing per larva is reduced to approximately two, the newly hatched larvae no longer produce developing eggs, but rather go through normal pupation and emerge as winged adults; these reproduce only after fertilization of their eggs and typically fly away from the home patch of fungus.

The same relation has repeatedly been shown in aphids. Wingless females reproduce parthenogenetically until environmental conditions deteriorate. Wings and the necessity for fertilization tend to develop concurrently.

It seems fair to state that almost all invertebrates have some mechanism for withdrawing from one environmental situation in order to appear in another. This mechanism may involve actual movement through space, as in the swarming of social insects and the dispersion of Daphnia in low algal concentrations (Smith and Baylor, 1953); or it may simply involve a retreat from physiological activity into a temporary state of dormancy, as in the diapause of insects and resistant egg formation in copepods, Cladocera, coelenterates, Platyhelminthes, etc.

Sexual reproduction occurs occasionally in all animals. In most species, although not in most individual organisms, sex is obligatory for reproduction. This is related to the dependence of speciation on reproductive isolation between groups of sexually reproducing animals. In a sense, speciation is a by-product of sexuality (*cf.* Fisher, 1958). The obligatory sexuality of most species can be considered a reflection of the changeable character of environmental conditions. I do not believe it accidental that so many of the small aquatic species are parthenogenetic, or at least not completely dependent on sex for reproduction. The air medium, with its low viscosity and low specific heat, is a much more variable one than water or soil. The mechanisms of establishment of obligatory sexuality are not clear, but they seem to relate to a dependence of the egg or the female on physiological stimulation from either the sperm itself or the male in order to initiate development of the egg.

This argument is presented here merely as a suggestion. Extended studies on the occurrence and mechanism of sexuality, particularly in the flatworms, would be necessary before the mechanism and adaptive significance of obligatory sexuality could be explained. It is clear, however, that many species do become obligatorily sexual. Some of these secondarily develop parthenogenesis, and it is of interest to note that the conditions of development of secondary parthenogenesis seem to involve ecological situations in which the normal environment of the species is a temporary one. This is true not only of some of what Hutchinson (1951) refers to as fugitive species, which have very high values of r but very low powers of resisting competition from other species, but also of species, like many of the aphids, that occupy an ecological niche that disappears completely in a short time because of noncompetitive factors in the environment. Plants in the temperate zone coarsen as the growing season terminates, and the nutritive condition of the aphids may correspondingly deteriorate. Rapidity of reproduction seems to be more valuable than the diversity that accompanies sex in certain circumstances, although no species can permanently do without sex.

In vertebrates, migration and wandering of individuals—either as a response to social pressure from the group or as a general response to environmental conditions—is extremely common. Burrell (1927) reports mass migration by platypuses during periods of drought. Errington (1946) discusses the wandering of homeless animals from crowded areas. In a study by Strecker (1954), five pairs of adult mice were liberated in a basement storeroom at the University of Wisconsin in 1948 and again in 1949. In 1948, 500 g of food were supplied per day; in 1949, 250 g of food were supplied per day. In 1948 the population size and food consumption per day by the population was constant until the termination of the experiment. In 1949 food consumption per day increased until all of the food supplied was being consumed, at which time the mice began to leave the storeroom and spread throughout the building. There was no diminution of the reproductive rate of the sort that had been found by both Strecker and Emlen (1953) and Southwick (1955) or in the various other studies of populations in sealed containers (Slobodkin, 1954a; Armstrong, 1960, etc.). The lack of surplus food apparently caused in the animals a behavioral response of emigrating.

Although in the above cases (the Daphnia, Oligarces, house mice) there is a clear relation between incipient food diminution and emigration either in time or in space, this is not necessarily always the case. Purely psychological factors may induce the tendency to move. King, in his study of the prairie dog town, believes that the emigration of adult members of a coterie to found a new colony is caused by their being continually badgered by playful young animals to the degree that their other activities are interfered with. The transition from the sedentary to the migratory phase in some of the locusts seems to be mediated through the central nervous system (Kennedy, 1937); in fact, the migratory locusts are excellent examples of species that combine many of the features we have discussed. Several of the plague locusts show two distinct "phases": the solitaria, or solitary, phase characteristic of low-level populations, and the gregaria, or gregarious, phase characteristic of dense populations. Gregaria typically has lower water content, higher fat content, darker color, and longer wings than solitaria; all of these properties make gregaria capable of longer sustained flight than solitaria. In a single species of locust not only these two extreme phases but a range of intermediate types may be found. In addition to the morphological differences, the two types differ in their behavior in the presence of other locusts. In the solitaria phase, locusts tend to come to rest near inanimate objects rather than near other locusts; gregaria-phase individuals preferentially rest near each other. In the gregaria phase the animals are apparently stimulated to marching and flying by the presence of other locusts to a greater extent than are individuals in the solitaria phase. Both forms migrate, but the solitary form keeps shifting its position so as to stay in essentially the same set of temperature, humidity, and vegetational conditions. The normal habitat vegetation dries up slowly as the year progresses, and the locusts follow the retreating greenery. The migratory flights of the solitary phase locusts occur primarily during the night. The gregarious phase of the same species migrates much more rapidly, with little regard to these environmental conditions, and flies primarily by day. Solitaria-phase individuals can be partially transformed into gregaria-phase individuals by seeing, and possibly by "smelling," other locusts (Norris, 1954). The effect is presumably mediated through the endocrine system. Offspring of gregarious individuals tend to be either gregarious or more easily made gregarious than offspring of solitary individuals. The mechanism of this is not clear. In the absence of males, locust females may produce eggs parthenogenetically.

The general picture of the population dynamics of the locusts, then, is that solitaria-phase individuals live in relatively moist vegetational areas, moving relatively little and, if necessary, reproducing without sex. As the environment becomes drier they tend to follow the vegetation and as they become more abundant some of the individuals take on some of the characteristics of the gregaria phase. These characteristics are self-reinforcing and the gregaria individuals begin to take longer and more frequent daytime flights, leaving the solitaria individuals behind. Swarms of gregaria are apparently transported and concentrated to some degree by wind movements and particularly by convergences (Rainey, 1951), thus producing the enormous swarms that are a major agricultural disaster wherever they occur. The solitaria individuals are capable at any favorable time of starting the whole process again, and if gregaria individuals are maintained for a sufficiently long time in solitary conditions they, too, will revert to the solitaria phase.

Extremely high concentrations of organisms of a particular species, as for example the locust swarms, are usually temporary or involve animals that are engaged in large-scale lateral movement. This must be so since, as we will see later, the relation between the rate of energy fixation by photosynthesis and the rate of energy utilization for maintenance by animals is such that tightly crowded together animals cannot conceivably survive by eating what grows between their feet.

The natural American bison herds were an example of a population that existed in very dense local accumulations but was absolutely dependent on extensive lateral movement of the herd as a whole in order to get food. It seems possible that the stampeding reaction of large cattle is related to this food requirement, since the animals at the middle and rear of a large, slowly moving herd will always live on an extremely low nutritional level unless the herd occasionally speeds up its movement. (This possibility was suggested by F. E. Smith.)

Huge numbers of animals of a particular kind sometimes appear suddenly in parts of the world. Certain cases, like the locusts or the red tide, seem to represent accumulation and transport of organisms by physical concentration devices. They do not represent a population growing and maintaining itself at the region of its occurrence.

The red tide outbreaks are particularly interesting from this standpoint. A red tide on the Gulf coast of the United States typically consists of an extremely dense population of dinoflagellates. The dinoflagellates are a group of protozoans that can photosynthesize to some degree but cannot, in general, survive on an inorganic medium; they therefore resemble animals in that they require some preformed organic material in their diet. During red tides the dinoflagellates occur in the surface water of the Gulf of Mexico in concentrations of six million organisms per liter and even higher, coloring the water to a red or chocolate color. Since these are fairly large protozoans, the implication is that relatively high values of phosphorus and other inorganic nutrients exist in the Gulf. In actual fact, however, the Gulf of Mexico in this region is singularly low in nutrients, and we are faced with the apparent paradox that red tides float in the Gulf but the Gulf cannot produce them. The paradox disappears by the following theoretical argument.

Consider an organism that occurs only sporadically in a mass of water and is not readily grown in the laboratory. The physiological requirements of this organism, whatever they may be, are obviously not met by the whole mass of water. Imagine that we pour some culture medium of a kind appropriate for growing red tide organisms into the Gulf of Mexico. Could we then develop a red tide population? We could not if we used only a small amount of culture medium, since it would mix immediately with the normal Gulf of Mexico water. If, however, we poured in a sufficiently large quantity of culture medium we could develop a red tide before the water of the Gulf diluted the medium too badly. The more rapid the rate of multiplication of the red tide organisms and the lower the rate at which the mass of culture medium mixes with the Gulf of Mexico water, the smaller the volume of culture medium needed to permit increase in the protozoan population. The general relation has been shown by Kierstead and Slobodkin (1953) as

$$L = K\sqrt{D/r}$$

where L is a linear dimension of the suitable water mass, D the rate of diffusion of this water into the nonsuitable water, and r the intrinsic rate of natural increase of the dinoflagellate population. K is a constant that varies with the shape of the suitable water mass, being equal to π (3.14 . . .) if the water mass is linear and leakage occurs only at the ends, and equal to 2.4048 if the water mass is a cylinder with leakage occurring from all sides. The relation is similar to that of critical mass in the construction of an atomic pile. If the mass is too small it is impossible to maintain a chain reaction against leakage. Using this formula in a rather simple-minded way it was possible to explain the paradoxical character of red tide outbreaks. Whatever else might be required by the red tide organisms, if they are to persist in the Gulf of Mexico the diffusion rate between the water in which they could survive and the normal water of the Gulf must be relatively low. One way of reducing diffusion is to have the boundary of the suitable and unsuitable water mass represent a boundary between waters of different density. That is, it is easier to mix two kinds of water if they both have the same temperature and salinity. The work of mixing required is only that necessary to overcome friction. If the two water masses differ in temperature and salinity the work of mixing required is much greater, since the lighter, warm, low-salinity water will tend to float on the heavier, cold, high-salinity water in the same way that fat floats on chicken soup. We might, therefore, guess that red tide organisms prefer warm, low-salinity water. If this is so, then red tides should occur in relatively wind-less hot weather, since the wind does the mixing, after heavy rains. We might also expect that they should occur only near shore where the fresh water can mix with salt water in river estuaries and embayments and then be disgorged into the Gulf as large masses of warm, low-salinity water, seeded with red tide organisms from the bayous and loaded with inorganic nutrients from the land. This argument has since been shown to be valid (Slobodkin, 1953b; Chew, 1953) in the case of the Florida outbreaks and probably a similar pattern is followed by outbreaks in New Zealand (Bary, 1954). Various dinoflagellates have now been cultured in the laboratory by

Provasoli, Hutner, and McLaughlin, and their co-workers at the Haskins Laboratories. The general culture requirements agree with those inferred from field distribution, and specific vitamin requirements, particularly of the vitamin B_{12} group, also have been demonstrated (Hutner *et al.*, 1956). Vitamin B_{12} is abundant in muds and swamps.

Other local dense accumulations of marine organisms are known that do not rely on land drainage but seem to depend, at least in part, on the existence of zones of convergence between oceanic water masses or, as in the case of floating masses of the blue-green alga *Trichodesmium erythreum,* convergences of surface wind patterns. Recall that locust swarms are also collected along wind convergences.

Some dense aggregations of territorial vertebrate animals arise by the animals collecting food from an area much larger than that occupied by the aggregation. Sea bird nesting colonies are of this type. Some of these not only gather food from large areas but rely on oceanic or meteorological mechanisms to concentrate nutrients and food for them, in the region surrounding their aggregation sites. This is the mechanism of dense population maintenance of the various sea birds on the guano islands of the South American west coast. The coast of Ecuador and Peru is characterized by continual upwelling of deep, cold water that brings nutrients from the dark depths up to the light where they can be utilized by phytoplankton; very heavy populations of microcrustacea and fish are thereby supported that, in turn, feed the birds. Any nutrients that sink out of the surface water in the central basin of the Pacific eventually return to the lighted surface by an upwelling process. The guano birds are therefore living on a concentration of nutrient material from a very wide area of the ocean. When, for any reason, the oceanographic or meteorological mechanisms for nutrient concentration temporarily fail, the dense bird aggregations disperse and apparently migrate in all directions and for considerable distances. This has been noticed most particularly in the guanays. Occasionally, peculiarities of weather develop that send warm water down the South American coast. At these times rain follows on the normally arid coasts, the upwelling ceases, and red water may appear. The birds then desert their nests and they have been picked up several hundred miles from their normal locations. This phenomenon, known as El Niño, since it usually occurs around Christmas time, has been described in detail in publications by Murphy (1923), Hutchinson (1950), and others.

We have seen that not only is the simple logistic equation inapplicable to metazoans but that the various more realistic forms of the population growth equation, based on life table data and specific physiological information of various sorts, although adequate for prediction in the laboratory, become difficult to apply in nature. A laboratory population is maintained in a sealed container whereas natural populations have various degrees of openness to their ecological niche. They may have regular migrations, specific escape reactions, dispersal patterns, and so on. All of these reactions are, in principle, predictable from a proper theory of evolution and to a certain extent are predictable from life table data. If life table data imply that population growth will be extremely unstable in the laboratory, it may be safely predicted that the species in question will have great openness in its ecological niche in nature.

chapter eleven

▸ Interactions between
Metazoan Species

So far we have considered only single-species populations of metazoans. We must now investigate interactions between species. The direct interactions between a pair of species can be only of five sorts: (1) the two species may compete for some resources of their environment; (2) the first species may serve as an environmental resource for the second; (3) the second may serve as an environmental resource for the first; (4) the two may be of mutual benefit; and (5) the two species have nothing whatever to do with each other (the null case). We will deal with these in sequence.

Despite the complexities that departure from the logistic curve lends to single-species population growth, the interspecific interaction patterns are most conveniently discussed in terms of the conclusions we have already derived from the elementary theory of interspecific competition.

The first possible outcome of competition, indicated in our earlier discussion, was that in which either of the pair of species might win in competition and the probability of a particular species winning was dependent on the initial relative concentrations of the two species. This situation has been found in the interaction between flour beetles (*Tribolium castaneum* and *T. confusum*) and has been analyzed in detail by Neyman, Park, and Scott (1958) using the data of Park. This probably represents one of the only metazoan competition experiments that has received adequate enough replication to make statistical theory formation possible.

The experiments were set at all possible combinations of three temperatures, 24°, 29°, and 34° C, with two humidities, 30 percent and 70 percent. At the lowest temperature and humidity *T. castaneum* was unable to maintain itself at all, even in the absence of competition from *T. confusum*. At the highest temperature and humidity the mean population sizes maintained by the two species separately were not significantly different, but at all other combinations of temperature and humidity one species or the other maintained a larger population size. When the two species were put together in a competitive experiment, one of the two species was invariably eliminated in competition. Only in the highest and in the lowest temperature-humidity combinations was the outcome of competition between the two species completely predictable, *T. castaneum* being better adapted to the hot moist condition and *T. confusum* to the cool dry condition. The optima for these two species, as judged by the size of population maintained in the absence of competition, does not seem to be at more extreme temperature-humidity values than those used experimentally.

At any given temperature and humidity one species was competitively victorious more often than the other. There was a definite percentage of the populations, however, in which the outcome of competition was reversed. In one temperature-humidity situation, *T. confusum* generally defeated *T. castaneum* in competition (71 percent of cultures becoming pure *T. confusum*), although when the species were raised in isolation the mean population density maintained by *T. castaneum* was somewhat higher than that maintained by *T. confusum*. The overall patterns of competition are represented by a set of empirical diagrams that effectively replace the diagram of Case 1 (Fig. 7-1) by a statistical picture in which line *OS* is replaced by a broad zone of possible initial numerical combinations of the two species. From any point in this zone either species may eventually defeat the other, whereas in regions outside of this zone the outcome of competition is completely fixed (Fig. 11-1). Neyman *et al.* drew the figures empirically from the data by plotting on a graph with ordinate *T. castaneum* and abscissa *T. confusum*. All the data from populations in which *T. castaneum* would eventually win are denoted by one symbol and all the data from populations in which *T. confusum* would win, by another symbol. The barriers of the zone of indeterminacy are the lines separating the region where both symbols occur from that where only one occurs.

It seems possible that within the zone of indeterminacy there is a differential probability of survival of the two species, depending on the initial concentration. If this is so, then the diagrams of Neyman *et al.* are probability of outcome surfaces, introducing

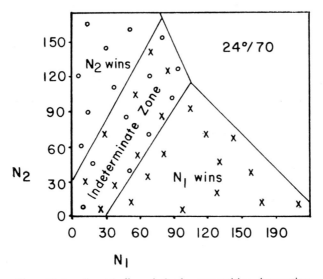

Fig. 11-1. Empirically derived competitive interaction diagram for two species of beetle (N_1 *Tribolium confusum*, N_2 *Tribolium castaneum*). The crosses and circles diagrammatically represent combinations of the two species found in experiments. If a mixed population once achieves a position in the area marked "N_1 wins" or "N_2 wins," the outcome of competition is predictable. Seventy-nine percent of the experimental populations at 24° C and 70 percent humidity eventually contained only N_2. (Adapted and redrawn from Neyman *et al.*, 1958.)

stochastic processes into the Gause Case 1 diagram shown in Fig. 7-1. It is of interest that the zone of indeterminacy is altered both in shape and position by environmental circumstances. Under the highest humidity and temperature, for example, the indeterminacy zone disappears, for although this regime is ecologically tolerable to both species only *T. castaneum* can persist through competition; on the other hand, the cool dry situation is not in the ecological niche of this species. The fact that in at least one environmental situation *T. confusum* wins in competition more often than *T. castaneum,* whereas in the same environment *T. castaneum* maintains a higher population when alone, is extremely important in indicating that the mechanisms of interaction within the single species are not quantitatively identical with the mechanisms of interaction between species, or at least are not quantitatively identical in their effect.

The population level of each species living alone is in part determined by the ratio of fecundity to egg cannibalism. A species with relatively lower egg cannibalism and fecundity may be able to maintain a higher population level than one with higher egg cannibalism and fecundity, but it may not be able to maintain itself competitively against the destruction of its eggs.

The flour beetle studies just discussed offer a metazoan example of one of a pair of species winning in competition as a function of environmental variation and, in some cases, as a function of a combination of stochastic processes and initial concentration.

\ Some experiments on competition between brown hydra and green hydra (*Hydra littoralis* and *Chlorohydra viridissima*) now being conducted in my laboratory provide an example of two species surviving together indefinitely under one set of environmental conditions but one being eliminated when the environment is altered. The animals of both species can be maintained indefinitely in an artificial salt solution. *Artemia* nauplii are used as food and both species of hydra require animal food for survival. The populations are maintained in 30 cc of liquid in Petri dishes. In the light the green hydra develop populations of about 5 to 10,000 animals and the brown hydra develop populations of 1 to 2000. The individual brown hydra are heavier than the green hydra by a factor of approximately 2 or 3 when they are in a crowded population. Under conditions of extreme starvation, however, the brown hydra can become extremely small and may lose their tentacles, becoming unable to feed readily. In the dark the population of brown hydra stays the same, but the green hydra can maintain populations of only 1 to 2000 animals, and these are extremely pale in color. Since the animals are fed and washed every day they cannot be kept in complete darkness, and thus the green color in what I have called darkness does not completely vanish from the hydra but it is attenuated.

In competition in the light both the green and the brown hydra increase in number and decrease in individual size initially. The food per animal therefore is reduced and the percentage of the Artemia consumed increases rapidly. Finally a carpet of brown and green tentacles lines the bottom of the dish and the number of Artemia per hydra decreases to one per week. The brown animals become reduced in size somewhat more severely than the green and are finally shut out from the food by a screen of green hydra tentacles.

The green hydra have available to them the subsidiary photosynthetic energy source of algae in the endodermal cells, and this may explain why their size is reduced less rapidly and drastically by starvation than that of the brown animals. In the dark the algae disappear, or at least no longer give a dark-green appearance to the animals. The green hydra therefore appear pale and thin, but they do persist, at least for the 6 to 10 months of the experiments. Possibly there is enough incident light during the counting, feeding, and washing process to supply the green hydra with their own ecological subniche. As the light intensity increases, the niche of the green hydra expands to overwhelm that of the brown.

There have been other experimental situations in which the investigator has been unable to alter the outcome of competition by altering environmental conditions. For example, in the experiments of Frank on competition between *Daphnia pulex* and *Daphnia magna* (Frank, 1957), *Daphnia magna* became extinct in competition in the presence of *Daphnia pulex* regardless of whether the food consisted of algae or yeast. Presumably there is some range of environmental conditions not known to the investigator, under which *Daphnia magna* would win in competitive interaction.

Although we can say that the conclusions derived from the elementary theory of competition generally are shown to be valid by various experimental tests, the statement must be qualified. The elementary competition theory, as formulated by Gause, Volterra, Lotka, and others, demands that the individual species populations grow according to the logistic curve, and metazoan populations do not usually grow in this way. However, at the state of population growth in which both species are crowded, many of the assumptions implicit in the logistic curve are no longer significant. For example, the logistic curve requires that the physiology of the animals in the population respond instantaneously to environmental change. When competition is taking place, however, environmental changes typically occur so slowly that the physiology of the organism has ample time to keep pace with them. It is only in the early stages of population growth, when the environment is basically empty, that changes in the environment are likely to occur so rapidly as to make physiological time lags, as experimentally demonstrated by Frank (1960), quantitatively significant. The term "environmental change" is here used to mean the environment of each individual animal; the main mechanism of environmental change will be changes in the number of animals in the container, or, in the case of interspecific competition, changes in the kind of animal likely to be directly or indirectly encountered—where "indirectly" refers to an encounter with the results of another animal's activities. The physical parameters of the ecological space, insofar as these are determined by factors outside the animals themselves, are assumed to be held constant.

Another assumption implicit in the logistic theory is that age-structure phenomena are not of significance in population growth. As we have abundantly demonstrated, in general this is not valid. When a population is close to a steady state, however, age structure is effectively constant. It is not as quantitatively significant during the competitive period as during the period of initial invasion of the environment.

In short, the results of interspecific competition—namely, elimination of one species, or persistence of both species with greater or lesser reduction of one—constitute all the possible outcomes of two-species competition and are almost independent of the growth form of the individual species. Interpretation of these results is essentially the same as the interpretation discussed in connection with classical interspecific competition. If two species persist in a particular region it can be taken as axiomatic that some ecological distinction must exist between them and that their ecological niches, in the restricted sense, do not coincide. If, on the other hand, one species is eliminated by competition the implication is that the ecological niche of this species was included in the ecological niche of its successful competitor. The one remaining possible situation—that is, two-species competition where the outcome depends either on the initial concentration of both species or on the concentration of both species that arises at some early period of population growth—is the one discussed with reference to flour beetles by Neyman, Park, and Scott (1958) or by Hutchinson (1947) with reference to social birds. We interpret this situation to mean that there are social interactions between the members of each species that will alter the magnitude of the species' effect on each other.

So firmly entrenched is this mode of thinking about interspecific competition that when two species are found to persist either in the laboratory or in nature, the investigation of the interaction between them is considered incomplete until the ecological distinction that permits their continued coexistence can be demonstrated.

The Gause axiom is neither an empirical statement that is subjected to empirical test nor an assumption underlying studies of interaction between species, but rather a rule of ecological procedure. This rule may be stated as follows:

Given a region of physical space in which two species do persist indefinitely at (or close to) a steady state, there exists one or more properties of the environment or species, or of both, that ensures an ecological distinction between the two species, and if one were able to construct the multidimensional, fundamental niche of these two species a region would be found in this multidimensional space that is part of the fundamental niche of one of the species but not of the other; and similarly, a region would be found that is part of the fundamental niche of the second species but not of the first. It would further be the case that the physical space in which the two species persist indefinitely at, or near, their steady state, represents a real-world projection of those portions of the fundamental niches of the two species that are not identical. If they seem identical the study is incomplete. (Get more data!)

This interpretation of the Gause axiom has led to various ecological studies in nature designed specifically to demonstrate the ecological differences between species that seem ecologically similar on superficial examination. Among the recent investigations of this type is that of MacArthur (1958) on the ecological distinction between five closely related species of warbler, all of which co-occur in the region studied although their geographical ranges are not completely identical. It was found by field observation that feeding behavior differed among the five species, particularly with reference to the mobility of the species. The amount of time spent perching, the portion of spruce trees investigated by the birds, and the manner of investigation also varied from species to species. Two of the species (the Cape May warbler and the bay-breasted warbler) were variable in year-to-year abundance. MacArthur concluded that the Cape May warbler depends on periods of superabundance of food. The myrtle, black-throated green, and Blackburnian warblers, on the other hand, had a relatively constant population size and seem adapted to food supplies and ecological conditions less variable than those of the Cape May and the bay-breasted. The myrtle warblers fed predominantly in the lower portion of spruce trees, the black-throated green fed in the middle portion of the trees and on the outer part of the branches, and the Blackburnian fed toward the top of the same trees and on the outer tips of branches. The Cape May warblers fed on the new growth on the top edge of the trees, and the bay-breasted fed throughout the trees, concentrating on the old growth close to the trunk. The method of hunting for insects on the spruce trees varied: certain species moved predominantly up and down the tree, others moved around the circumference of the tree, and the Blackburnian and the bay-breasted moved predominantly in and out from the trunk of the tree.

There is now an abundance of field studies, all of which give roughly the same type of conclusion—namely, that any two species found to coincide in residence do show slight differences. Depending on the interpretation the investigator chooses to give to the data, these are or are not considered sufficient to guarantee ecological-niche differentiation. Some of these distinctions are extremely delicate. For example, several species of fruit fly larvae have been found inhabiting the same peach, but extraction of yeasts from their guts demonstrates that each species has fed on a different species of yeast. Reindeer herds in northern Canada and Alaska move more slowly than caribou herds, with the result that the reindeer herd completely denudes the pasture area of its slowly growing reindeer lichen. It takes many years for the pasture area to recover. The barren-ground caribou, on the other hand, move rapidly enough so that the herd never completely denudes a pasture area. The recovery of the land from this type of feeding is much more rapid than the recovery from the feeding activities of reindeer. It is fairly common to find large and small species of filter-feeding crustaceans coexisting in a lake (Hutchinson, 1951, 1959). The large species are presumably feeding on somewhat larger diatoms and flagellates than the small ones. A superficially similar relation is found in various insular regions populated by many species of birds. Typically, size is a differential between sympatric populations of different species. This has been most carefully noted by Lack (1947) in the finches of the Galapagos Islands. We will return to this when we talk of the theoretical construction of models of entire communities.

To some degree, investigations that demonstrate an ecological distinction between two species of different appearance are tauto-logical. It is clear from elementary considerations of the mechanisms of evolution that the morphology of a species is determined by natural selection. This means, in effect, that the ecological history of the species is to some extent preserved by the evolutionary process. Anyone who has kept a cat or a dog as a pet knows that the behavior of their particular animal is somewhat different from the behavior of other cats and dogs in the neighborhood. If we imagine a species composed of individuals identical with my cat and another species composed of individuals identical with the cat next door we would find that these two species differ in their feeding habits, hunting habits, and behavior. We could, if we so desired, point to these differences and say that we have verified the Gause axiom and that the two species would continue to coexist because of the observed differences in behavior.

It is clear that all species are morphologically distinct, and, since morphological evolution is adaptive, morphologically distinct species would be expected to be ecologically different. What is not yet clear is the degree of ecological difference required to permit coexistence, and we are not even sure how this difference should be measured. It seems likely that observed behavioral, morpho-logical, and physiological differences between two species should be considered in the light of their effect on the passage of energy and nutrients through the two populations. The degree of ecological difference between two species that will just permit coexistence will vary from species to species. It will depend on the energy require-ments for maintenance of a stable population by each of the species and on how the other species alters the effective concentration of energy available to the population. There are situations in which it may be expected that groups of ecologically very similar species may persist together indefinitely.

We cannot exclude the theoretical possibility of at least a temporarily benign environment or of an environment so variable that the struggle for existence outlined in our competition equations can never come to completion (Hutchinson, 1953). An outstanding example of the latter type of environment is that formed by the top several meters of many temperate lakes in the summertime.

By the early summer many temperate-zone lakes develop a rather strong temperature gradient (thermocline) across a fairly narrow stretch of water that will be between two and 10 meters from the surface. Above this zone the water is relatively warm; below it the water is cold, in some lakes as cold as $4°$ C. Winds blowing across the lake mix the surface waters down to, but not below, the temperature gradient. The water is full of microscopic plants, particularly diatoms and some flagellates, which are all bathed in the same solution. The water is chemically homogeneous above the thermocline. Individual plant cells are stirred through the entire water mass several times during the course of the day, and so the light intensity on each cell is effectively constant. As many as 10 or 20 different species may occur simultaneously in this extremely homogeneous environment. As the summer proceeds, the relative abundance of the different species may vary slightly, and occasionally some species may even disappear. If, however, a sample of this upper water is taken out of the lake and placed in a bottle in a laboratory, the richness of species diminishes very rapidly. The implication here is that in nature slight changes are occurring in the environment with sufficient rapidity to make it impossible for any species competition interactions to go to completion; that is, the system is out of equilibrium all the time. This may be generalized in terms of the effect of the environmental fluctuations on a single species.

Each species tends to act as a frequency analyzer for fluctuations in its environment (Slobodkin, 1954b). Imagine an environment fluctuating at random, and consider this environment to be occupied by an elephant population. Fluctuations with a time periodicity of hours or days would be of very little significance in controlling the size of the population, but fluctuations of the order of 10 or 15 years might be. If the same environment is also occupied by flies, which seems extremely likely, the fly population may be responding to temperature fluctuations of the order of five to 15 days, and small mice in the same forest might be responding to fluctuations of the order of three years.

If two species are simultaneously occupying a spatial region in which there is a broad area of ecological overlap—and hence we might expect the Gause situation of species competition to be realized—and if this environment favors first one species and then the other with a time periodicity of a generation length in both species, it is quite likely that a permanent nonequilibrium situation will occur. If the periodicity of the environmental fluctuations are very much shorter or longer than the mean generation time of each species it would be expected that the competition would come to its theoretical conclusion. In this case, only one species would persist, unless the environment actually did contain two ecological niches.

We have already mentioned several examples of the escape mechanisms available to populations of single species. There seem to exist species so well adapted to escape and recolonization that they can survive in nature by invading temporarily vacant ecological situations, although they are removed from these situations by competition in a relatively short time. Such species have been termed fugitive species by Hutchinson (1951), and they seem to be much more common than Hutchinson's original suggestion would imply. In particular, Daphnia and many other of the Cladocera seem to be able to invade a lake or a pond with great rapidity in the early spring, being later almost completely eliminated as the more slowly increasing zooplankton organisms increase their pressure on the environment. All species that are most commonly found in preclimax ecological situations and are invariably absent from the ecological climax may, to some extent, be considered fugitive species.

If several species are co-occurring in an area where all of the nonreusable, time-dependent variables of the environment are superabundant but each species is separately limited by some reusable time-independent variable, it is possible, over some levels of population density, to have an ecological steady state in which coexistence may occur. Imagine a situation in which several species of birds maintain territories, and assume that a bird considers a territory filled only if it is occupied by a member of the same species. Each species may then be limited by available territory area but no two species can compete if other ecological variables are superabundant. This situation, if it exists, is unstable since at any time food may become limiting. Further, if a sufficiently large number of species is present, the actual space for nests, courtship, and so on will become limiting. Competition in the classical sense will follow, presumably with elimination or ecological differentiation of the various species concerned.

In tropical rain forests there is a tremendous diversity of plant and animal species, and typically individual specimens of a particular species are not clumped as they are in temperate forests. Somewhat speculative explanations can be produced that would maintain the Gause axiom intact. It can be imagined, for example, that each particular species of tree requires in its ecological niche the presence of other species. This would be true of a form that requires shade during its entire growth period. Another possible explanation is that soil competition for nutrients is minimized in a plant assemblage of several species. Nutrients are known to be very rapidly utilized in tropical forest, and the various species in a mixed assemblage would be less likely to be surrounded by individuals with precisely the same nutrient requirements as their own. It is also possible that because of the extremely long generation time of forest trees, disturbances such as burning, or even climatic change, may be preventing the establishment of equilibrium.

The Gause axiom is clearly applicable to laboratory and certain field situations. It is true that laboratory situations require the addition of a stochastic term to describe the outcome of competition, that some field situations are difficult to explain in such a way as to conform to the Gause axiom, and that occasionally the explanations are quite frankly speculative. The abandonment of the Gause axiom, however, is equivalent to abandoning the concept of competition, and competition is the only reasonable mechanism developed to explain the generally homeostatic properties of the natural world. As indicated in a comment by Skellam (1957), in the absence of some feedback mechanism or some homeostatic mechanism in populations we must assume control of population size by random variables. The extinction rate actually observed in nature is much smaller than that implied in the concept of random controlling variables.

Up to now we have been discussing the interaction between individual organisms in a population and the interaction between populations of species that may compete with each other for some environmental resource but do not live by eating each other. We will see later that the distribution and abundance of entire communities in nature is of the sort that would be expected on the assumption of the Gause axiom and not the sort that would be expected on the assumption of control by random environmental variables.

chapter twelve

Prudent Predators
and Efficient Prey

The steady-state values of mean population size in nature or in the laboratory do not represent equilibrium values in the usual sense. A pendulum is at equilibrium when it is hanging vertically. Work must be done on the bob to make it take any other position or to make it swing, but no work need be done to create an equilibrium position. Similarly, a solution of three chemical compounds, A, B, and C, in which the conversions

$$A \rightleftharpoons B \rightleftharpoons C$$

are possible will, after sufficient time has elapsed, have the equilibrium concentrations K_A, K_B, K_C, and it will be possible to alter these concentrations only by supplying energy to the system in the form of heat or electricity. Nonliving equilibria are stable states that systems come to in the absence of a supply of work or energy from outside the system.

Ecological steady states, on the other hand, are contingent on energy being supplied at a steady rate to the system from outside. If this supply of energy is cut off, the system can no longer maintain a steady state but comes to chemical and physical equilibrium; that is, it dies. Steady states, as distinct from equilibrium, are also possible for nonliving systems. For example, a steady-state distribution of temperature occurs in a metal bar that is strongly heated at one end only. A steady-state distribution of water pressure occurs in a system of plumbing pipes that are suitably connected to a pump and water supply. At first glance, these may seem to provide analogies for the steady-state distribution of potential energy found in ecological communities. These analogies can be misleading, however, since only the ecological community depends on energy flow for its physical integrity. The plumbing does not dissolve as soon as the water is turned off at the pump, nor do wires vanish because a circuit is broken; but the bodies of organisms die as soon as the transport through them of potential energy ceases.

Since the process of maintaining a living population requires a continual flow of potential energy, the size of any animal population will depend on the rate at which potential energy enters the plants or animals that serve as its food and on the proportion of that energy that the population can consume. A prudent predator will consume its prey in such a way as to maximize its own food supply while at the same time minimizing the possibility that the prey population will be unable to maintain itself and serve as food in the future. In a sense, a predator must use its prey efficiently. Predators, like all organisms in nature, seem to behave with great prudence, but this apparent prudence is purchased at the cost of endless evolutionary experiment that is expensive in lives. We will try to state the theory of predation demanded by the natural world, toward which all predation must evolve.

Radiant energy is absorbed by green plants and part of this is converted to potential energy by the process of photosynthesis. The slow conversion of this potential energy to kinetic energy permits ecological communities to survive. Considering sunlight to be the primary energy source of the ecological world, we consider plants to be on the first trophic level, animals that live exclusively on plants to be on the second trophic level, carnivores that eat only herbivores on the third trophic level, and so on. Competition is an interaction between animals on the same trophic level and is, in a sense, a horizontal interaction. In addition to horizontal interactions there are extremely important vertical interactions.

When a predator consumes its prey, or when a fishing boat removes fish from the sea, or when a hunting party kills a part of a reindeer or caribou herd, we can say that the prey population is being used, as a machine for converting some portions of the world that are relatively abundant but not particularly useable into some more useful form. For example, if eaten directly, plants are not useful forms of energy for cats. Cats may occasionally eat members of the mint family as general stimulants, in the same way as humans may eat arsenic for their complexion or their wind, but the tooth structure of a cat is such that chewing plants is impossible for the animal. From the viewpoint of a cat, mice are machines for converting plants into food. A rational cat will not want to eat all of the mice in a sealed barn because a certain number of mice must be left behind to replace the mouse population. But it can be expected that a rational cat will want to exploit the mouse population in such a way as to maximize the quotient

$$\frac{\text{calories of mice eaten by cats}}{\text{calories of grain eaten by mice}}$$

This ratio is the efficiency of the mouse population at making cat food.

Just as the work load placed on a steam engine may be varied, thereby varying the efficiency of the engine, so the population may receive heavier or lighter external loads in the form of predation, and its efficiency will vary accordingly. A significant difference that can be found between a steam engine and the mouse population or any other appropriate biological working machine is that the living system must use part of its energy to manufacture and repair itself. The efficiency of the mice in the mouse-cat case depends not only on the physiology of the mice but on the behavior of the cats and the kind of grain provided for the mice. Efficiency, in this sense, although it is referred to as the efficiency of mice, is actually a function of three different species. The number of mice and of cats present at any one time is referred to as the standing crop. There is no immediate simple relation between standing crop of mice and their efficiency.

Let us slightly modify our analogy. Rather than a storehouse full of grain, imagine a chute down which the grain pours, the mice snatching grain as it goes by and the cats snatching an occasional mouse. This is, of course, a much more realistic situation. Here the efficiency of the mice depends not only on the kind of food provided but on their effectiveness at catching the grain. (In principle, the mice could, by being appropriately numerous and adroit, catch and consume all of the grain.) In this case, the ratio

$$\frac{\text{calories of mice consumed by cat per unit time}}{\text{calories of grain passing down the chute per unit time}}$$

will be called the food-chain efficiency of the mice and the ratio

$$\frac{\text{calories of mice consumed by cat per unit time}}{\text{calories of grain consumed by mice per unit time}}$$

will be called the ecological efficiency of the mice. The food-chain efficiency becomes identical with the ecological efficiency when no grain is permitted to reach the bottom of the chute; the greater the proportion of the grain that reaches the bottom of the chute the greater the difference between the two efficiencies. Ecological efficiency will always be equal to or greater than food-chain efficiency.

The cats will be concerned with maximizing their total food consumption; that is, with consuming as many mice as possible each day without depleting the mouse population to such an extent that tomorrow's mouse crop is endangered. But even if the cats could decide on an appropriate rate of mouse catching with only this objective in mind, they may not have solved all of their problems. For example, they might find that optimal mouse yields are associated with such small mouse populations that much of the grain falls to the bottom of the chute. We can imagine rats eating this grain, terriers eating the rats, and chasing the cats. It is therefore of possible advantage to the cats to maximize the proportion of the total grain eaten by the mice. This may require leaving such a large mouse population behind that the yield of mice per day will be seriously lowered. Designing a proper mouse exploitation program is not simple.

It may be expected that a predator's population size will be influenced by the food supply provided to it by the prey and hence by any fluctuations that may occur in the prey population. Correspondingly we may anticipate that the prey population will be affected by fluctuations in the predator population. For the sake of simplicity we will momentarily consider that the predator is removing prey at a constant rate and we will explore the problem of the effect on a steady-state prey population of various kinds and intensities of removal by a predator. Recall that in a steady-state population $\sum l_x m_x = 1$. The process of predation can be considered as an alteration of the l_x term. That is, predation adds to the prey species a new source of mortality, in addition to the mortality that arises from other sources. Therefore, if a new steady state is to be achieved under predation, either the m_x distribution or the l_x distribution of the surviving animals must be altered by the predation process. The simplest case to visualize is that in which only m_x distribution is altered.

In experimental Daphnia populations subjected to predation, removal of some animals increases the food available for the others and thereby increases the reproductive rate, restoring a new steady state at a somewhat lower standing crop. In the blowfly, on the other hand, the m_x distribution of surviving animals is not seriously altered by predation. Predation that is sufficiently severe to lower significantly the number of breeding individuals will also lower the intensity of larval competition and thereby alter the l_x distribution, restoring the steady-state condition (Nicholson, 1957).

Any species in which neither the l_x nor the m_x distributions are alterable as a consequence of predation will be unable to return to a steady state and may be expected to become extinct. If we imagine some prey population in which neither survival nor fecundity are functions of population density and in which the condition $\sum l_x m_x = 1$ is met, the only way of exploiting this population would be for the exploiting agency to replace the existing sources of mortality on the species. If, for example, we were dealing with a deer species that was inflexible, the only safe exploitation procedure would be to follow some other predator—say a panther—that preyed on deer, predict in some way whether the panther would be successful in killing any particular deer at any particular moment, and then capture that deer immediately before it is acquired by the panther. Fortunately, for most species there is some flexibility in l_x and m_x and there is abundant evidence, as indicated previously, that density-dependent factors do control population size, at least in part, in all species.

Any alteration in survivorship produced by a predation system automatically competes to some extent with other sources of natural mortality. When the rate of predation on a deer herd is low, mortality from starvation and disease is correspondingly increased. The relation is similar to competition between diseases. If the advance of medical science makes certain diseases less virulent or makes the lethal effects of such diseases as whooping cough, scarlet fever, and measles relatively low, it must automatically and at the same time increase the lethal effects of accidents and other diseases. The effect of predation on the size of the prey populations is either to substitute one cause of mortality for another or to lower the survival at some particular age in the population, or both. If the predation simply substitutes one mortality cause for another it would not be expected to produce any physiological changes in the prey population. If, however, the survival at some age is reduced by predation there will be a compensatory change either in the survival at some other age or in the fecundity of the prey species, or the prey species will become unstable and probably extinct. The effect of predation on standing crop size in the prey species will depend in a very precise and definable way on the efficiency with which organisms are produced by the prey population and on the l_x distribution.

A machine, in general, is designed and constructed to do a particular kind of work or to produce a particular form of energy. The ratio of the output to the input (both in energy units) is the efficiency of the machine. The output of a moving locomotive is in the energy used to overcome the forces that tend to stop the train; the input is in the potential energy of coal or oil burned in the process. The output of a light bulb is in visible radiation; the input in electric energy and the ratio of the two is the efficiency. Notice, however, that it is possible to read by the light of a coal locomotive's firebox or to warm oneself at a cloth-draped light bulb. These are not particularly clever ways to read or to keep warm, but they are conceivable. In these terms, the efficiency of a locomotive would be measured as the ratio of visible radiant energy from the firebox to potential energy consumption, and for most locomotives this efficiency is lower than the initial calculations of its efficiency; the efficiency of the light bulb would be measured as total radiant energy output over total electric energy input and this ratio would be higher than the original estimate of the bulb's efficiency. We can conclude from this that the magnitude of an efficiency does not necessarily have anything to do with the importance of the process to which the efficiency ratio refers, even in the case of a machine.

It is meaningless to refer to "the efficiency" of a population. The term must at all times be qualified. We can speak only of the efficiency of producing energy in some form that we arbitrarily consider useful (the output) from some other form that we arbitraily define as useless (the input).

An organism must do many things that require energy. Movement of its internal parts, movement of itself in its environment, production of new protoplasm to compensate for attrition of its body, addition of new protoplasm to its body, and production of offspring—all are energy-utilizing processes involving single organisms. On the level of the individual we will be concerned with the efficiency of the last two of these only. In the following discussion, therefore, only new protoplasm will be considered as an ecologically useful kind of potential energy and other possible uses of energy on the individual level will be largely ignored.

Although all organisms depend ultimately on radiant energy, the form of energy that is transferred from organism to organism and effectively keeps ecological systems running is potential energy, as stored in organic molecules. We will find it convenient, on occasion, to speak of energy as flowing through a population. The limits of this metaphor must be clearly stated, however. Energy first enters an animal population through the mouth of an animal and it leaves the population either as heat, or as the potential energy of a dead animal or of feces, or by entering the mouth of a predator. The flow of energy through a population is highly turbulent at best. We will consider the useful energy output of any population to be in the form of edible animals and we will consider the energy input to consist of food eaten by the population.

The energy content of a Daphnia or a Chlamydomonas cell can be measured in terms of the heat released on combustion (Richman, 1958). Using the combustion data of Richman, it was possible to perform the following experiment in my laboratory.

We maintained Daphnia populations from which animals were removed at a regular rate. Since we knew the energetic value of the food provided to the Daphnia populations and the energetic value of the yield of Daphnia, we were able to compute the efficiency of the populations at converting algae into yield. To make sure that the populations would be able to persist under the removal procedure the number of animals removed from each population was a fixed fraction of the number of animals born in the population.

A procedure for determining the number of animals to be removed does not limit the kinds of animals that are removed. Adult animals were removed from some populations and young animals from others. Populations subjected to the first procedure were called adult removal populations and those subjected to the second procedure were called young removal populations.

After maintaining the populations for a sufficiently long time we had direct information for each population on the average number and size distribution of the residual population (P_F) and the average number and size distribution of the yield at each census. Using the analyses of Richman these numbers can be converted into calories (energy units). We also determined the food supplied the population in terms of photometric units of algae. By counting the algal cells in samples of the food suspensions we determined the number of Chlamydomonas cells fed to the populations. Multiplying this figure by Richman's estimate of the number of calories per algal cell gave us an estimate of the calories of food provided to the population. Not all of the populations ate all of the algae provided. We estimated the proportion of food eaten by each population in an indirect way (cf. Slobodkin, 1959).

In other studies Richman (1958) and Armstrong (1960) determined the food consumption and growth rates of individual Daphnia.

With all this information we evaluated three significant concepts of efficiency in Daphnia. The simplest, and the most important for community interactions, is the ratio of the energy content of the animals removed from each population to the energy content of the food. When we consider the energy of the food supplied we are dealing with food-chain efficiency, whereas when we consider the food eaten we are dealing with ecological efficiency.[1] Ecological efficiency is determined by the rate of removal of animals and the proportion of the food consumed that

[1] The terminology used here may not be in complete conformity with all of the published discussions. An attempt to collate terminology has been made by MacFadyen (1957), but it would take too much space to analyze here.

can be converted into animal calories. It has no direct relation to the size of the population from which the animals are removed. As would be expected, very low rates of removal result in low food-chain and ecological efficiencies. Higher rates of removal result in higher efficiencies. Excessively high removal rates, however, reduce the population to such a degree that it is unable to consume all of the food provided, and food-chain efficiency therefore decreases. The maximum food-chain efficiency found in the Daphnia populations is around 8.5 percent and the maximum ecological efficiency is 12 to 13 percent.

Field estimates have been made of ecological efficiency by entirely different methods. A typical field estimate will involve the following procedures and calculations:

(1) The species in a community are assigned to trophic levels. All green plants represent one trophic level, all herbivores the next trophic level, all carnivores that eat only herbivores the next, and so on.

(2) The total food consumption, in calories, of each trophic level is estimated.

(3) The ecological efficiency of trophic level x, which is fed upon by trophic level $x + 1$, is the food consumption of trophic level $x + 1$ divided by the food consumption of trophic level x.

Rather large sampling errors are involved in the several stages of the field efficiency estimates, but surprisingly, the observed values from the field are essentially identical with the maximum values observed in the laboratory. Ten estimates from field data have been collected from the literature by Patten (1959). Except for one value of 75 percent (Teal, 1957) and one of 21 percent (Lindeman, 1942) all of these estimates range from 5.5 percent to 13.3 percent. There is no significant relation between trophic level and efficiency in the other eight values. Notice that the top trophic level in any community has an ecological efficiency of zero by definition. The agreement of the laboratory estimates with the field estimates indicates that the various assumptions made in the field have been surprisingly accurate. It also indicates that for all practical purposes ecological efficiency can be considered a constant. It may be expected that future field estimates will tend to converge on some relatively narrow range of values around 10 percent.

Additional factors that should be considered are the relation between the animals removed from a population as yield, the size of that population, and the energy consumption of the population. These can be studied by means of the population efficiency. If the process of removing animals does not alter the energy consumption of the population, population efficiency can be expressed as

$$E_{pi} = \frac{Y_i}{I(1 - P'/P)}$$

where E_{pi} is the population efficiency associated with removing Y calories of yield per unit time with an age composition i in the yield animals. I is the energy consumption of the population in calories per unit time, P' the caloric content of the population at its steady-state value under the removal procedure, and P the calories in the population if no removals are made.

If food consumption is altered by predation

$$E_{pi} = \frac{Y_i}{(\text{maintenance cost per time of } P') - (\text{maintenance cost per time of } P)}$$

Notice that maintenance cost per time of an entire population is equal to the energy consumed per time, since the yield animals are, from the standpoint of the population, simply other corpses that must be replaced if a steady state is to be maintained.

A steady-state population maintains numbers of animals, age composition, and size distribution constant. In order to do this, the size and age distribution of the corpses produced by the population must be constant. The process of maintenance of the population is, in one sense, the process of maintaining a constant supply of dead animals of the appropriate age and size. Maintenance cost per unit time is the sum of the energy costs of producing all of the individuals that die during that time.

If an animal age i has a caloric content S_i, and if the calories required for the replacement (or equivalently, production) of such an animal are S_i/E_i, then E_i is the efficiency of the production process. E_i will be called the growth efficiency or individual growth efficiency.

Growth efficiencies have been calculated by Armstrong (1960) and Richman (1958) for *Daphnia pulex*. Following Armstrong, growth efficiency is evaluated as follows:

(1) Food consumption and caloric content of a single animal as a function of age is determined experimentally.

(2) For the age interval t, $t + \Delta t$ immediately prior to the beginning of reproduction,

$$E_{t,\Delta t} = \frac{\text{caloric content}_{t+\Delta t} - \text{caloric content}_t}{\sum\limits_{t}^{t+\Delta t} \text{food consumption}}$$

is computed.

(3) On the assumption that $E_{t,\Delta t}$ is constant during the reproductive period, the energy cost of producing a single egg can be computed. Armstrong determined the food consumption and growth during reproductive life. The total energy utilized for growth could be determined by dividing the calories of growth by $E_{t,\Delta t}$. Subtracting this from the total energy consumed as food and dividing the total calories of newborn by this difference the cost per calorie of egg was determined. Multiplying this by the calories in each egg gave the total cost in calories of each egg.

(4) The quotient

$$\frac{\text{calories of animal of age } i}{\text{cost of an egg} + \text{food consumption from birth to age } i}$$

is the efficiency of growth up to age i.

Growth efficiency, unlike population efficiency, is a property of the individual animal rather than of the population. Armstrong (1960), using his own data and those of Richman (1958) and Slobodkin (1959), has determined growth efficiency as a function of size of animal and concentration of algal cells in the medium. Since Daphnia, like most other animals, grow most rapidly when young, growth efficiency up to any particular age decreases with age. Daphnia make feeding movements of their legs whether or not any food is caught; hence if algal cells are excessively dilute, the energy expended in feeding is disproportionately high. When algal cells are too concentrated, they pass through the gut without being thoroughly digested. There is, therefore, an optimal algal cell concentration for growth efficiency. The results of Armstrong are summarized in Fig. 12-1.

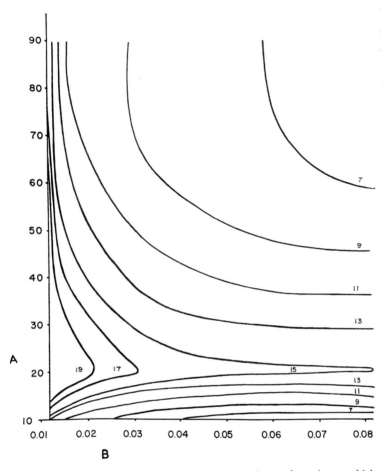

Fig. 12-1. The efficiency of growing a *Daphnia pulex* to the point at which it has a specific caloric content, as a function of algal cell concentration. The ordinate is concentration of *Chlamydomones reinhardi* cells in thousands per ml. The abscissa is the calories released on combustion of the individual Daphnia. The contour lines are the percent efficiencies of individual growth. (Unpublished material printed with the kind permission of Dr. Joseph T. Armstrong.)

Maintenance cost in a population will depend on the number of animals that die, their age distribution, caloric content at the time of death, and the efficiency with which they can be replaced.

Removing animals as yield alters the age-at-death distribution to a greater or lesser degree and may even alter the efficiency of growth. In general, the greater this alteration, the greater the effect on population size. Removing animals that are about to die will have almost no effect on maintenance cost, whereas removing animals that have a long life expectancy severely increases population maintenance cost, and consequently diminishes population size.

If appropriate data are available, the population efficiency associated with any predation procedure can be evaluated in terms of change in population size, energy consumption, life expectancy, and growth efficiency. If yield, population size, and energy consumption data are available for several populations, it is possible to solve for the population efficiency that would be associated with a predation procedure that removed only one size or age category of yield animals. In a sense, population efficiency can be computed as a function of age.[2] When this was done for Daphnia populations it was found that the highest population efficiencies were associated with the oldest animals and the lowest population efficiencies with the youngest animals. Note that this is the reverse of the relation between individual growth efficiency and age but might have been expected from the survivorship curve of Daphnia. The value of the concept of population efficiency cannot be determined until more species have been analyzed. Its interest lies in the fact that it relates yield production to population size and therefore permits us to outline the most efficient procedure for a predator. A prudent predator should take yield organisms in such a way as to maximize its yield and at the same time maximize the population efficiency of the prey.

[2] The procedure is simple but tedious. It involves making best least squares estimates of E_{pi} in a set of equations involving sums of products of the calories of yield of the various ages i and of the calories remaining in the population (cf. Slobodkin 1959, 1960).

chapter thirteen

Predator-Prey
Interactions

Throughout the discussion of predation in the preceding chapter we assumed a prudent predator who will only diminish the size of the prey population and who will be very careful not to make it impossible for its prey to return to a steady state. There is abundant field evidence and a fine theoretical formulation by MacArthur (1955) to indicate that the stability of a predator-prey system is increased when a relatively large number of prey species are available for the predator. Typically, predators feed on the most abundant food species available at any particular time, and as soon as this shows any signs of scarcity they switch their feeding preferences. It will be of interest to examine a very simple experimental situation and see what happens when a predator and a prey are simultaneously introduced into a sealed container. This is the classical predator-prey system extremely popular with nonbiologist mathematicians because it shows convenient cyclic properties. One of the forms the model can take is

$$\frac{dN_1}{dt} = r_1 N_1 - \gamma_1 N_1 N_2$$

$$\frac{dN_2}{dt} = \gamma_2 N_1 N_2 - d_2 N_2$$

where species N_2 is the predator and N_1 the prey. The loss of the prey population depends on the frequency of contact between predators and prey and on the fraction of those contacts, γ_1, that result in a lethal effect on the prey. In the absence of prey the predator should die at the rate d_2 and the population of the predator should increase in proportion to the contact between the prey and the predator, at a rate γ_2. The predators at any given moment represent an accumulation of the products they have acquired from the prey in the past; thus time dependence is introduced into the system, thereby permitting oscillations.

Unfortunately, this system seems to be unrealistic in the case of micro-organisms. Gause (1934) has done a major study of this equation, utilizing the ciliate *Didinium nasutum,* which voraciously and dramatically feeds on paramecium. He found that unless periodic additions of new prey and predator animals from outside the container were made, the system was unstable because of the elimination of the prey by the predator and subsequent starvation of the predator. Occasionally, the rarity of the prey resulted in starvation of the predator, in which case the prey went to equilibrium. The number and frequency of immigrant organisms required to generate oscillations varied with the level of spatial heterogeneity maintained in the container. Specifically, if a culture of paramecium was maintained with an oatmeal sediment into which the paramecium, but not the didinium, will enter, the oscillatory patterns predicted by the predator-prey equations had some likelihood of occurrence, particularly if occasional introductions of new didinium were made. The periodicity of the oscillations found in the experiments was not identical with the periodicity of immigration into the container. To this degree there is biological validity in the cyclic property predicted by the mathematical formulation.

These experiments introduce the important concept of spatial heterogeneity as such being a significant factor in the regulation of kind and number of animals in nature. The stability properties of the predator-prey equations and some of the modified forms of these equations have been discussed in detail by Lotka (1934), Kostitsyn (1937), and Volterra (see D'Ancona, 1954). Huffaker (1958) has shown in an extremely elegant experimental system that predator-prey oscillations, in the absence of immigration, can be reproduced in the laboratory in a two-species system if there is extensive spatial heterogeneity in the environment. He used the six-spotted mite

Eotetranychus sexmaculatus as prey, and as predator he used the mite *Typhlodromus occidentalis*.

The prey species fed on oranges in the laboratory. When the predator was introduced onto a single, prey-infested orange, it completely eliminated the prey and then died of starvation. Huffaker arranged a series of paraffin stands on which oranges were placed in a large rectangular tray. The oranges were covered with lint. The environment could be altered spatially by covering portions of the oranges with typewriter paper or paraffin, or by substituting for oranges lint-covered rubber balls, which were apparently searched over by the predator as if they were oranges, although they contained no prey organisms. Oranges were replaced as they became unusable for the prey, but never at a rate of more than one quarter of the oranges per census interval. In the absence of predation, prey could maintain itself quite satisfactorily regardless of the dispersion of exposed orange surfaces on the rectangular grid. When both predator and prey were present, the population histories varied, depending on the spatial distribution of oranges, balls, and uncovered areas on each orange.

In the simplest situation, food was concentrated in one portion of a tray. There was an early initial rise of prey, followed by a very rapid rise of predators, followed by depletion of the prey and finally starvation of the predators. The prey were not actually eliminated but were reduced to extremely low numbers. After the predators had starved, the prey population increased to control population size.

As the food was more widely dispersed over the trays the time lag between the initial rise of the prey population and the major rise of the predator population increased. Small pockets of prey occurred on oranges that had not yet been discovered by wandering predators. In a situation in which a small quantity of food was very widely dispersed over the possible universe there was a rather long persistence of both predators and prey at very low population levels. Even here, eventually, the predators starved to death.

Huffaker then increased the complexity of his universe in an effort to produce the theoretically possible predator-prey oscillations. In general, mites will not cross lines of Vaseline drawn on the surface of the tray. Three trays, each with 40 locations for oranges, were joined together. Oranges were placed at all 120 of the possible locations. The available feeding surface on each orange was reduced to $\frac{1}{20}$ of the orange's surface. A maze of Vaseline lines was drawn between the oranges. Even in this complex system, if the predator and prey were both introduced in the same general region, the history of the predator-prey relation was similar to those previously discussed. Neither the predator nor the prey managed to get past the various Vaseline barriers into the other available feeding areas on the trays.

When, using the same arrangement of the trays, Vaseline lines, and oranges, the prey were initially introduced at the rate of one mite on each of the 120 oranges and the predators were also introduced in a widely dispersed fashion, repeated fluctuations of predators and prey occurred. Huffaker maintained a population of this sort for eight months. During that time there were three major increases of prey, each one followed by a major increase of the predator and a reciprocal decrease of the prey. At the end of eight months the predator almost eliminated the prey, the predators starved to death, and the prey started to increase.

Simplifying the results somewhat, the mechanism of the continued oscillation was as follows. Whenever a predator individual came in contact with a population of prey, the predators increased locally and the prey were eliminated. The predators then diminished at that location and began to wander into other areas. When predators became sufficiently scarce, the prey individuals increased locally and developed considerable local populations before they were encountered by wandering predators. When the predators moved in, the process was repeated.

In the individual subareas of the experimental universe, the prey was either increasing in the absence of predation or very rapidly decreasing if predators were present. In other areas of the universe, reciprocal events were occurring. The periods during which, in the universe as a whole, a predator population was extremely large were characterized by a relatively large number of individual foci of prey being attacked by the predator, while a few foci of prey infestation had not yet been discovered. The periods of low predator population were characterized by a relatively large number of areas occupied by prey, a few areas occupied by wandering predators, and a few areas occupied by both predators and prey. Toward the termination of the experiment most of the areas occupied by prey were also occupied by predators, and this resulted in the essential collapse of the rather tenuous, unstable equilibrium. Food supply was limiting to the prey only during the last major population increase.

From this remarkable set of experiments it may be inferred that spatial heterogeneity, as such, tends to stabilize ecological communities and that heterogeneous spatial distribution of the prey, in a situation in which the food supply of the prey is uniformly distributed, implies that the prey is controlled by predation. The local survival of the prey depends on the chance of encounter of predator and prey, and the increase of heterogeneity simply increases the chance that at least some prey individuals will not be encountered by the predator.

In a set of field experiments Huffaker and Kennett (1956) found that the application to strawberry fields of chemical pesticides that killed both the cyclamen mites that infested the strawberries and the predatory mites that consumed the cyclamen mites resulted in increased cyclamen mite populations and considerably lowered yield and vigor of the strawberry plants. The same result obtained in greenhouse tests. In this situation the cyclamen mite apparently reinvaded the fields much more rapidly than its predator. If predator and prey were simultaneously introduced into a greenhouse patch, both predator and prey persisted on the strawberry plants at a low level, resulting in very little damage to the plants. If chemical pesticides were used and predator mites then introduced, the predators simply starved to death.

When predators are present, cyclamen mites generally can survive only in the more sheltered portions of the strawberry plants. In these regions they cannot do serious damage to the strawberries, and once they venture out of their sheltered localities into those portions of the plant where damage can be done, they are consumed by the predator. In short, a natural refuge exists, permitting stability of the predator-prey system.

Huffaker and Kennett suggested the possibility of infesting strawberry fields with both cyclamen mites and predators to encourage the development of low-level population equilibrium of both species. This rather startling suggestion has, to my knowledge, not received extensive field trials as yet. It is of particular interest, however, since it represents one of the first practical suggestions for establishing an ecological equilibrium in nature that will be advantageous to an agricultural or other human development. It is in sharp contrast to the more customary approach of maintaining lack of equilibrium by rather strenuous human efforts.

These results are in surprisingly close agreement with those of Errington (1946) in populations of mammals. As a result of many years of extensive field study he has concluded that the only mammals that fall prey to predators are those that, in some sense, are out of place in their natural environment. Mammals that do not have home territories or that are in transit from one region to another because of a local excess fall prey to predators. Those that are established in the social structure of their own population and that have clearly defined runs, territories, or burrows are almost immune to predators.

Lack (1954) has considered the reciprocal relation and he believes that the pressure exerted by a predator on a population is very closely related to the other prey available to that predator. In particular, during periods of heavy rodent infestation the population of rodent predators seems to increase. If and when the rodent populations decrease, a predator may increase its level of predation on other prey that are not normally attacked.

In summary, then, the elementary predator-prey interaction equations predict the occurrence of rather regular and reciprocal oscillations between a predator and its prey in a simple environment. These oscillations can only be produced in the laboratory with elaborate immigrations of both predator and prey, or with extremely complex experimental situations in which spatial heterogeneity is deliberately introduced into the population's environment. There is evidence from both laboratory and field work that in a heterogeneous spatial environment it is quite likely that the prey normally has some refuge available and that oscillations, if they occur, are of relatively low amplitude. Certainly, in the absence of refuges, the entire predator-prey interaction is unstable.

It has occasionally been proposed that reciprocal predator-prey oscillations are not generally found in temperate regions because of the stabilizing effect of alternative prey species and the general complexity of temperate communities. It has therefore been suggested that the reciprocal oscillations that occur in the far-northern Arctic between jaegers and owls on the one hand and various species of lemming and other small microtine rodents on the other constitute a classical predator-prey interaction.

Extensive studies by Pitelka (1957) and his co-workers indicate that the lemming oscillations are not caused by predation. If anything, the predators exert a damping effect on lemming oscillations. The normal pattern of lemming (*Lemmus trimucronatus*) growth in the Point Barrow region of the Arctic seems to be an increase during the winter under the snow, and a decrease, due to predators and low food supply, early in the summer. This is followed either by a slight increase or by at least a cessation of the decrease in the late summer when predators, particularly jaegers and owls, have completed breeding. When the lemming population is low, the survival of vegetation through the winter seems fairly good, the jaegers fail to breed, and snowy owls breed only sporadically. Apparently, excessive lemming population destroys local vegetation and jaegers and owls breed only when there is an ample supply of lemmings for food. The lemming population increase starts at the end of the summer and continues throughout the winter.

A one hundred-fold increase in lemming population occurred during the winter of 1951–52 in the Point Barrow region. At the time of the melt in 1952 the grass was heavily cut by lemmings in the elaborate runway systems that had been made under the snow. The predators were breeding and feeding on lemmings and they reduced the lemming population by more than half by the middle of July. New grass began to appear late in the summer and the predators departed, permitting a slight increase in the lemming population until the snow arrived and a moderate increase during the following winter. The population effectively doubled in the winter of 1952–53. After the melt of 1953 the grass was almost completely cut and the runway systems were much longer and more complicated than they had been the previous year.

At melt time after the second winter of population increase, cover and food for the lemmings were typically almost completely absent in local areas. The lemming population declined throughout the summer because of the combined effects of starvation and predation. This decline was so rapid that occasionally the predators were not able to breed successfully, even though it was a peak lemming year. Since at the end of a summer of lemming population decline the grass was still almost absent, a decline in numbers of lemmings continued through the following winter, except for isolated, particularly favorable pockets of vegetation. The following summer there was a return to a very low lemming population with abundance of vegetation present.

Typically, then, there is a three-year lemming population cycle. Starting at the low point, at the first winter, there is approximately one lemming to every five or 10 acres. During the first summer, there is an increase of lemmings and an almost complete absence of predation. This stage is followed by a very strong increase under the snow cover of the second winter, a slight decrease in the second summer, an increase under the snow during the third winter, and an almost catastrophic decline during the third summer. This decline continues into the beginning of the fourth winter, returning again to initial low population level and completing the cycle. The population density of lemmings at their peak is approximately five hundred times that at the low point.

In local areas, the three-year cycle as outlined can be shifted to a four-year cycle by anything that will slow up the increase during the second or third winter. In particular, Pitelka reported (in conversation) that in the winter of 1956 there was a sudden thaw followed by a hard freeze. Lemmings without burrows were found wandering over the frozen surface and heavy death occurred prior to the melt time. The populations did not crash that summer as was expected on a three-year cycle assumption, but increased during the following winter and finally crashed during the summer of 1957. It is possible that heavy predation during the increase periods would forestall the catastrophic population declines for one or more years, although direct evidence of this is lacking. In 1949 lemmings were found dead or in convulsions at the time of the melt, but this phenomenon was not often encountered in other years.

It is abundantly clear that the declines in the lemming population in the Point Barrow region are not caused by an excess of predation. In fact, the mechanism of fluctuation in this population is very similar to that we have previously discussed in connection with populations of Daphnia and blowflies. Pitelka reports that the lemmings do not, in general, migrate outward in the Point Barrow region except, perhaps, during the last stages of starvation. It will be recalled that migration and escape were normal reactions in many organisms, acting to prevent acute population oscillations.

To the degree that the predators make the rate of lemming increase during the second and third summer lower than it would normally be, they are acting to damp the oscillatory pattern by making the period of the oscillations somewhat longer. Further data are now being collected on the lemming populations by Pitelka and the story is by no means complete.

Cyclicity in lemming populations is local, not extending over regions in which we might expect to find any astronomical three- or four-year cycles. The entire cyclicity is describable in the same general context that we have seen in the laboratory for Daphnia and blowflies. The cycle length in lemmings is essentially determined by the life expectancy of the animals and the time required for a population to increase up to a point of collapse. It seems at least possible that similar arguments can be used in other cases where cyclicity of populations has been reported in nature. The entire subject of cycles, however, has become extremely complex and controversial, and we will examine it more closely in the next chapter.

chapter fourteen # The Reality
# of Cycles

The instantaneous size of any population, as we have demonstrated, is dependent on environmental circumstances and on the physiology of the individual organisms concerned, and to some extent on the past history of the population as represented by its age structure and the condition of its various members. Among the environmental features that alter size are the various variables we have indicated in our definition of ecological niche—particularly weather, food supply, and predators. We have seen that theoretically and in the laboratory more or less regular oscillations in population size can be induced, either by periodic fluctuations in environmental variables or, in some cases, even in the absence of such fluctuations. Regular semicyclic fluctuations can be induced by predation of suitable kinds, as well as by physiological inter-action in single species. To what extent are populations in nature subject to regular, periodic fluctuations? If periodic oscillations do occur in nature, what is their ultimate cause? It is quite apparent that fluctuations in population size do occur, but it is not as easy to determine whether they are due to the environment or whether they are, in some degree, intrinsic in the physiology of the species concerned.

Unfortunately, one of the most difficult things to determine about any animal population is its size in nature. Derivatives of growth curves and details of courting, mating, psychology, and evolution, which would seem fairly abstruse, are relatively simple to determine; but a complete numerical census requires simultaneous observation of the population over a large area and has been made for very few organisms. Consequently, it would seem that the appropriate procedures for testing the reality of oscillations in population numbers in animals would have to be either theoretical —that is, in terms of biologically realistic models—or experimental. We will deal with these approaches in that order. Note that a variety of techniques (tagging, release and recapture, counting of signs left by animals, and so on) permit an approximation to an actual census.

If internal oscillations do not exist in nature, it would be expected that observed fluctuations will be correlated with some changing factor in the environment. Since there are an infinite number of changing conditions, however, simultaneous measurements of the appropriate environmental and population change are difficult to make in any one research program. This is particularly the case if the environmental change is not on an annual basis or is something more complex or more difficult to measure than temperature, light, or humidity.

It can be assumed that there are no well-defined periodic oscillations in inanimate nature with a time periodicity of three to 12 years. It might be expected that any population that is fluctuating in response to nonseasonal environmental variables should show an essentially random fluctuation pattern. There is, however, a wide body of literature, some of it on the crank fringe, that claims to demonstrate the existence of three-, nine-, 11-, or occasionally 13-year cycles in nature. If we assume that the cycles of animal abundance in nature are actually random, how can we get this appearance of regularity? Part of the answer is that some of the data analyzed in these studies have been subjected to smoothing and other manipulations that produce a superficial appearance of cyclic patterns. A simple theoretical analysis of the properties of random number sequences (Cole, 1954b) will further help to explain the apparent contradiction.

Quite often the census data used to determine the apparent cycles are not particularly good. In fact, it may be possible to distinguish only between large populations and small populations. Consider a population that can be designated as large (L) or small (S) and then consider all possible three-year sequences—for example, SSL, LLS, and so on. There are eight such three-year sequences possible. Only one of these—namely, SLS—will be an apparent maximum in population size. The probability of three successive years representing a peak in population size is therefore 1/8 and the mean cycle length in a population of this sort is eight years. If three population levels are recognized there are 27 possible arrangements in a sequence of three years, of which five will represent a peak, and the mean cycle length will be 27/5 or 5.4 years. In general, if n levels of population size are distinguishable the mean length of a cycle m is given by

$$m = \frac{6n^2}{(n-1)(2n-1)}$$

This is essentially a three-year cycle when n approaches 100. The difficulties of field investigation make 100 significantly different levels of population size a very good population estimate indeed. Therefore, the mean length of a population cycle may be expected to vary between eight and three years as a function of the precision of the population size estimate, simply as an artifact of census inaccuracy.

It is also possible to induce an apparent cyclic pattern in populations by smoothing the data from successive years. At the limit this will result in a sinusoidal-type curve. Cole (1954b), following the mathematical analysis of Kac, has considered the effect of a weighted two-point moving average on the cyclicity of a random number series, where the weight of the present year is 1 and the weight assigned to the previous year is greater than 0 and less than 1—namely, w. A population peak is now defined by four years, Z_1, Z_2, Z_3, and Z_4, by the condition

$$wZ_1 + Z_2 < wZ_2 + Z_3 > wZ_3 + Z_4$$

In a period of N years there will be $(N-3)$ such groups of four years, and this will be one more than the number of cycles in the series. The probability that four numbers will determine a population peak, assuming that Z is accurate to four decimals, is dependent on w. When $w = 0$, the problem becomes the probability of drawing three random numbers with the largest one in the middle—that is, 1/3. When $w = 1$, the condition for four numbers to determine a peak is

$$Z_3 > Z_4 \quad \text{and} \quad Z_2 > Z_1$$

Each of these conditions has the probability of $1/2$, so that the probability of their combined occurrence is $1/4$. The number of peaks in a series of N numbers is $p(N - 3)$ and the number of cycles will be $[p(N - 3) - 1]$; whence the mean cycle will be

$$m = \frac{N}{P(N - 3) - 1}$$

In the case of $w = 1$ and $p = 1/4$, $m = 4N/N - 7$, which will be four years if N is sufficiently large. Four-year cycles are very commonly reported for small mammals. For values of w between 0 and 1, Kac (1954) has shown that

$$p = \frac{4 - w - w^2 + w^3}{12}$$

which Cole used to determine the mean cycle length in terms of N and w. Starting with random number sequences and smoothing with various values of w he determined the frequency of cycles of various lengths. He concluded that the cycles found to date are consistent with the hypothesis of random environmental factors being subjected to various values of w in the smoothing operation.

The interesting point is that the smoothing can be done either by the research worker confronted with a set of random numbers or by the organism itself confronted with the set of random extrinsic environmental oscillations. Implicit in the work of Cole and expanded somewhat by Hutchinson (1954) and Slobodkin (1954b) is the possibility that the magnitude of w is an echo of the fact that populations are feedback systems and that any such systems will of necessity act as a resonator, selectively responding to the fluctuations in the environment according to their time periodicity, the primary resonance being in the period of approximately one generation. The most obvious test of this concept will be a direct laboratory study in a controlled environment. Note, however, that the mere presence of out-of-phase oscillations in laboratory populations does not prove the concept. The laboratory is an unnatural world and therefore cannot completely simulate natural conditions; moreover, the intransigence of organisms being what it is, even the laboratory does not have the full advantages of the completely controlled system.

There is one partially analyzed experiment from my laboratory that seems to have some relevance to this problem. If a population is acting as a frequency analyzer to its environment, the frequency distribution of environmental fluctuations would be expected to change in passing through a population. For example, imagine a Daphnia population consuming, to a greater or lesser extent, a slightly fluctuating food supply; let the fluctuations of the food supply be random. We have already seen that when sufficient predation is exerted on such a population, the relation between the population and its food supply becomes such that food is always left over. Since it appears that water is not poisoned in any way by Daphnia, the leftover water from a population subject to relatively intense predation is a suitable medium for the growth of another Daphnia population. We will refer to the population that receives the initial unused environment as the host population and we will call the population that receives the environment after it has been filtered through the host population the scavenger population.

If we now use Cole's definition for a population peak in its most rigorous form, we can compare the frequency distribution of cycle lengths of host populations with those of scavenger populations. If Daphnia populations actually do act as resonators, the host population may be expected to absorb selectively certain frequencies of fluctuation in the food supply. If these frequencies have actually been absorbed by the host population, they should be lacking in the environment of the scavenger population and therefore in the cycle frequency distribution of the scavenger population. It should also be the case that the cycle lengths that are selectively absorbed by the host population should have some simple relation to the generation time of Daphnia.

When a comparison between the cycle-length frequency distribution in a group of scavenger populations was made, the only statistically significant difference found in the distribution patterns was that cycles of 16 days length were significantly less frequent in the scavenger populations than in the host populations. Since censuses were made at four-day intervals, the implication is a resonance period for the host populations of somewhere between 14 and 18 days, which is of the order of one generation time.

Unfortunately, this study of resonance now stands alone and not too much weight can be given it. Assuming, however, that resonance will be found in other populations, we can expect the cyclicity of populations in nature to vary in wavelength and amplitude and in the precise cause of death during the population decline. In the lemmings, starvation and predation seem of paramount significance. In voles and other small mammals it is quite possible that endocrine anomalies result from some complex combination of social and nutritional factors and seriously alter population growth (Christian, 1956).

The observed cycle lengths cannot be expected to be unalterable. In an environment that is varying in a random fashion, the smoothing pattern exercised by the ecological world in its response to the environment will vary from species to species. It may be expected, as pointed out by Hutchinson (1953), that the resonance period of any population is some multiple of the generation time. It is also possible that there will exist resonance periodicities in entire communities. Given a predator-prey situation, the more intense the predation, the lower will be the correlation between the prey species abundance and nonpredatory environmental factors. Predation, in effect, makes a population of prey individuals more dependent on their own physiological make-up than on fluctuations in the environment, and when predation is sufficiently high the population size will be related primarily to the parameter, r, the rate of natural increase that we have discussed above.

When a species does not alter its population size in response to a change in some environmental factor for which it is competing with some other species, it is certainly being controlled by some second factor that is quite likely predation. If we consider stability in a community to be defined as a function of a change of the total standing crop of all the species in the community, we would expect stability to be higher in a system in which two competing species are both preyed upon by one predator than in a system in which the predator is so specialized that it preys on only one species. Assuming constant ecological efficiency in the previously defined sense for the two competing species, under a given level of predation, stability in the three-species community would be expected to be maximal when the predator divides its efforts evenly among the two prey species. This would result in forcing both prey species into as close as possible a relation to their own physiological properties for population regulation. To the degree that either prey species still fluctuates with environmental change, the predator population will fluctuate unless it has alternative sources of food supply. Stability will therefore be expected to increase with the number of energy paths available to the predator.

MacArthur (1955) has formalized this concept and provided a theoretical framework defining stability of a community in terms of the energy pathways in that community. If a community is represented by a network of arrows such that the point of an arrow leads to a species and the tail of an arrow leads to some other species that is being fed on by the species at the point end, stability increases with the number of arrows in the food chain. Any increase in the number of species capable of maintaining a steady state in the community implies an increase in the stability of the community. Identical stability can be achieved either with a large number of species, each with a restricted diet, or with a small number of omnivorous species. Maximal stability arises when all species have an omnivorous diet.

The strength of the MacArthur formulation is in its rigor. Unfortunately, there is no immediate evidence that the quantity defined as stability by MacArthur's formulation has any relation to any common-sense definition of the concept of stability. Certainly, however, MacArthur's conclusions are generally in agreement with other ecological data. In particular, the cases of animal invasion collected by Elton (1958) indicate that invasions are most likely to be successful in communities that have low stability in MacArthur's sense.

We can conclude that observed fluctuations in populations and in communities are, at least in part, intrinsically regulated by the organisms themselves and are not completely dependent on environmental sources. In any case, they do not necessarily have any 1:1 correspondence with environmental fluctuations. It is not possible at the moment to say what proportion of the total population fluctuations occurring in nature is intrinsic and what proportion is due to the environment. Any attempt to attribute major importance to one factor or the other is probably premature.

Presented with the practical problem of distinguishing between the various possible kinds of fluctuation, we can make some tentative conclusions even in our present inadequate position. If some nonbiological environmental factor is found whose fluctuations correlate very closely with those of the species in question, there is no further discussion. For example, the correlation between red tides and meteorological conditions is such as to leave us with a very safe conclusion about a direct causality. If populations in nature are found to fluctuate in phase with each other over a very wide area, there probably exists some environmental correlate or set of environmental correlates. It is most unlikely that population interactions will occur between two individuals of any particular species that are extremely far away from each other spatially. Ideally, population interaction involves some sort of contact between the members of a population. If, on the other hand, nearby, but ecologically distinct, populations fluctuate out of phase with each other, the chances are that there exist some intrinsic phenomena of the sort we have found in the laboratory. This would be especially strongly indicated if the fluctuations are accompanied by changes in age structure.

The magnitude of a change in population size in nature probably depends not only on environmental changes but on the timing of these changes. An environmental alteration will have a much greater effect on population size if it occurs at some particularly critical time in the history of a population than if it occurs at a relatively insensitive period in the population's history. This is shown clearly in Pitelka's analysis of the lemming populations and their possible interaction with predators; only when predation was unusually heavy during the period of population increase was the natural periodicity of three years altered to four years. Another example is in the red tide, where, during the early stages, a slight change in natural phosphate concentration of the water will materially alter the probability of major red tide outbreak; once the red tide organisms are themselves killing fish, slight differences in nutrient concentration of the water become almost insignificant because the fish broth itself serves as a nutrient medium. Perhaps the most important conclusion from the investigation of population fluctuations is that there is no evidence whatsoever of occult or extramundane controls operating to produce regularities in the terrestrial ecological world.

chapter fifteen > Communities in
Nature

From our previous discussions it should be apparent that we could go from a study of two-species interaction to the theory of three-species interaction and finally to a theory of n species interaction, in which all of the species are on the same trophic level. We could also start with predator-prey interactions between a single species of prey and a single species of predator and then introduce two species of prey and perhaps two species of predator and continue to develop theoretical complexity, adding stability to the system as we go along (*cf.* MacArthur, 1955). Unfortunately we would have a fantastically complicated mathematical formulation before we were through and would rapidly exhaust our supply of relevant data. It is therefore desirable to develop a general theory that describes the steady-state properties of the entire community in terms of some elementary ecological assumption. Preferably such a theory should not depend on precise evaluation by censusing the number of individuals of each species, the number of species, or the number of actual specimens observed.

With almost any collecting procedure—for example, a light trap or a sweep net—a mixed collection of specimens can be acquired from any given region. For most such collections it will be found that a few species will be represented by a relatively large number of individuals and a large number of species will be represented by just one or two specimens. A tempting question, therefore, is whether the relation between number of species and number of specimens is at all constant in various collections. If the same distribution is found to hold for a wide variety of mixed collections of this type, the implication is that some underlying ecological law exists that is quite general in its applicability to various communities.

During the 1940s and early 1950s a variety of statistical distributions were fitted to field data on species-abundance distributions. Fisher, Corbet, and Williams (1943) observed that the number of species (S) caught by a light trap is related to the number of individuals (N) in the total sample by the equation

$$S = \alpha \log_e(1 + N/\alpha)$$

The larger the absolute value of the constant α, the greater is the diversity of species in the sample. The formula of Fisher, Corbet, and Williams provides an estimate of how many new specimens must be acquired by a given sampling procedure before a new species is encountered, on the assumption that α itself is independent of sample size. There is, however, evidence from the work of these three investigators, and others, that α does vary with sample size.

Implicit in this formulation is the notion that more species will be represented by only one individual than are represented by a larger number of individuals. However, a situation in which species represented by only one individual are less common than species represented by some larger number of individuals may equally well be visualized. Preston (1948) has therefore offered an alternative formulation for the relation between species and abundance. He considered that for each community there exists some modal abundance level. That is, while one community may have more species represented by one individual than by any other number, another community may have more species represented by five or even 10 individuals than by any other number. In a sense, this modal abundance is a characteristic of the community. The number of species in any particular abundance category can be expressed as a function of the number of species in the modal abundance category. If the abundance categories are grouped into successive powers of two, the number of species in each such grouping forms part of a normal curve that can be expressed by the equation

$$S_r = S_o e^{-(ar)^2}$$

when S_o is the number of species in the modal octave. The modal abundance category may represent all abundances from 2^3 individuals to 2^4 individuals, or eight to 16 individuals. The next category would represent all abundances from 16 to 32, the next from 32 to 64, and so on. S_r is the number of species r octaves from the mode, and a is a constant calculated from the data. The Preston formulation is more general than that of Fisher, Corbet, and Williams, but is still an empirical fit to an observed distribution. The constants α in the Fisher, Corbet, and Williams formulation and a in the Preston formulation not only change from community to community but also change with sample size in the same community. This indicates that neither of these distributions corresponds to a characteristic of the community being studied, but is in part characteristic of the sampling procedure and sample size.

MacArthur (1957) attempted to construct species-abundance distributions starting from ecological theory rather than from purely statistical properties of such distributions. He assumed three alternative ecological situations. The first, and most likely, from our previous discussion of interspecific interaction, is that each community consists of a group of species each one of which utilizes the environment in some way so as to make it completely unavailable to the other species in the community. In this model Mac-Arthur compares the environment to a stick of any given length that is broken by throwing single points at random onto it. The abundance of each species in the community is then considered to have the same distribution as would the lengths of the broken pieces of stick. If we start with a stick of unit length, the expected abundance of the rth rarest species, where there are S species and N individuals, is given by

$$\frac{N}{S} \sum_{i=1}^{r} \frac{1}{(S - i + 1)}$$

At this level this model corresponds to the assumption of the universal validity of Gause's axiom.

An alternative distribution can be constructed on the assumption of the complete falsity of Gause's axiom; namely, that each species is independent of all of the species of the community. Mac-Arthur uses the analogy of the stick and considers that pairs of points are thrown at random onto the stick and that abundance of a particular species can be represented as a distance between a pair of such points. In the distribution of species abundance generated by this paired-point hypothesis species of intermediate abundance are rarer than in the distribution generated by the initial hypothesis.

The third hypothetical distribution considered by MacArthur is generated by considering that ecological space is represented by particulate rather than continuous variables; that is, each species is considered to be represented by some sort of an urn into which particles of abundance are tossed at random. On this hypothesis, as the number of particles becomes large the relative abundance approaches identity of number of organisms in each species. This distribution is more rectangular in shape than the other two possible models.

Although the MacArthur distributions are by no means exhaustive, they are of particular interest since they represent three well-defined biological hypotheses and are amenable to field tests. Using bird census data of Quaker Valley, Pennsylvania, MacArthur found a closer correspondence with the first hypothesis—the one that assumes the Gause axiom—than with either of the other two. Kohn (1959), working with snails of the genus Conus in Hawaii, found remarkably close agreement with the first MacArthur distribution in some of his samples.

MacArthur notes that with some collections of data the common species are excessively abundant and the uncommon species excessively rare. He considers that this is because the sample includes two separate communities and that, properly, samples of this type may be taken to represent two sticks of unequal length, each representing the separate community. Hairston (1959), using data from the old field on the George Reserve, was able to test this hypothesis by combining data from the upland of the old field with data from the swale bottoms. As previously indicated, the uplands and swales are distinct communities by any sensible criterion of the concept of community. Hairston found that MacArthur's initial hypothesis came closer to fitting the data than either of the alternative hypotheses. Contrary to the conclusions of MacArthur, the fit to the distribution was closest for the smallest soil samples and was somewhat worse for larger soil samples and for the pooled data for the uplands or the swales taken separately.

When, however, Hairston pooled samples from the two communities the fit to the MacArthur distribution was found to be very close indeed. MacArthur's initial suggestion was that deviation from his theoretical distribution would be enhanced by community heterogeneity, but this is denied by Hairston's data. Hairston interprets his own data to mean that a natural community is a highly organized group of interacting organisms in which the relative abundance of the different species is not a random variable. He considered that the closeness of agreement with the MacArthur distribution obtained by pooling different communities is due to the fact that he had deliberately constructed a sample in which organization was low. To emphasize this effect Hairston constructed an imaginary community by pooling species-abundance data from a sample of marine phytoplankton from Spain and a sample of soil arthropods from Michigan. In this case, also, the pooled data was much closer to the MacArthur distribution than was either set of data alone.

From the work of MacArthur, Kohn, and Hairston it can be concluded that the overall distribution of species and abundances in fairly diverse natural communities agrees with the expectations derived from extending the theory of simple one-, two-, and three-species interaction situations to a large number of species in nature. It may also be concluded that communities in nature do not represent random numerical abundance distribution, but that the distribution pattern, as developed by MacArthur from the broken stick model, must be modified in some way to account for the departures from randomness.

It seems conceivable that the conclusions of Hairston and MacArthur may be mutually reconcilable on the tentative assumption that relative abundances of species on the same trophic level are random but that the mean abundance varies with trophic level in a nonrandom way as would be expected on the basis of our analyses of efficiency and predation. If this were the case, the explanation given by MacArthur of deviations from his model would be effectively valid; that is, a sample of an entire community including all trophic levels would actually consist of a sample composed of several sticks, each one in itself broken at random. Each stick would now represent a new trophic level. In the bird data, relatively small area samples would all be effectively on the same trophic level and in the same trophic relation to other members of their community. Given larger areas, enhanced deviation would be expected for the reason stated by MacArthur. Hairston's data, on the other hand, consisting as they do of soil arthropods in which certainly three trophic levels are represented, would tend to deviate from the MacArthur model unless the sample was very small. Combining data from different communities would, in effect, blur the trophic relations of each single community and, as Hairston points out, supply the randomness implicit in the MacArthur model in its simplest form.

An experimental test of this hypothesis has been made by Hairston. Taking single trophic level subsamples from his microarthropod data, he found that when the species-abundance relations in these subsamples are compared with the MacArthur distribution there is still a deviation and the deviation is in the sense of multiple stick environments. Hairston suggests (personal communication) that different taxonomic groups in the same community may represent different initial pieces of the community stick, in the MacArthur sense.

Although it is not made explicit by MacArthur which resource or resources in the community are divided between the species, it seems fairly clear (*cf.* Hairston, 1959) that whatever resources are divided must be completely nonrenewable and that the most significant nonrenewable resource is food energy. Members of a single trophic level or of a fairly narrow taxonomic group are more likely to compete directly with each other for food than with members of either different trophic levels or different taxonomic groups. The total energy resource of the community then represents the total stick. It is initially divided by the taxonomy and to some degree by the anatomy of the photosynthetic plants into several parcels, each one of which is divided among some group of organisms. These parcels might represent, say, leaves, seeds and wood. If we examined seed eaters in general we might find two, three, or perhaps four fairly broad taxonomic categories represented—for example, small passerine birds, small rodents, and orthopteran insects. It may be expected that the species-abundance distribution within each of these taxonomic groups will follow the MacArthur pattern, while all seed eaters will deviate to some degree and the entire community will deviate to a greater degree for the reasons already indicated by MacArthur. The closest agreement with the MacArthur distribution yet found is that reported for several occasions by Kohn (1959) in his work on the genus Conus, and here the requirement is met of identity of trophic level and relatively close taxonomic relation for all organisms composing the samples. There are not a sufficient number of locations, nor are there sufficient collateral data, to deny the possibility that agreement with the MacArthur distribution is simply fortuitous.

In developing the theory of populations we started our initial discussion with the causes of death in individual organisms and individual cohorts of organisms. Death and reproduction were combined in a generalized theory of population growth and we then dealt with population steady states as such. We found that we could make generalizations that would, to a large extent, transcend some of the ecological differences between species. MacArthur has now taken information on the continued existence of the steady state for small numbers of species, as derived from laboratory and field work, and extended it to steady states for communities as a whole. Granting that the extension is not particularly precise in detail, it still bears promise that it is in principle possible to make statements about communities as a whole that are somewhat more than mere metaphor. Perhaps the primary point of the MacArthur distribution and its method of development is that it indicates the broad path that ecological theory will probably follow in the future, and is indicative of a degree of theoretical maturity.

chapter sixteen ▸ Speculation

At present we have a great deal of data on the sources of mortality of a particular species, on the geographical distribution of particular species, and even in some cases on the population controls existing in particular species. All of these questions are extremely special and localized, and a description of the entire ecological world in terms of questions of this type would become inordinately complex. To answer simpler questions about the world as a whole—for example, why there are as many animals and species as there are in the entire cosmos, why communities typically have as many trophic levels as they do, and what the relation is between taxonomic and ecological composition in a community—we must have theories that fully utilize the complexity of the natural world in their construction but whose conclusions or theorems are extremely simple.

This problem has been handsomely analyzed by Margalef (1958) in terms of the information present in a community as it relates to the information content of the theory used to describe the community. Following the standard techniques of information theory, Margalef considers the total information present in an ecological community to equal the number of choices that must be made in specifying the complete condition of the community. As a simplifying assumption he considers that we have complete information about a community if we simultaneously know the number of species in the community, the number of individuals in each species, and the location in the spatial area under consideration of each individual of each species. The process of obtaining this information can be done in a stepwise fashion.

167

For any moderately large community the total number of choices involved in localizing the individuals by species—that is, in gaining the maximum information—is several hundred to several thousand times that required to identify the total number of species present, and the total information involved in setting up the species-abundance distribution is about 10 times that required to determine the total number of species. Notice that in general the definition of information involves determining the total number of choices required to specify which particular situation out of a given initial array of possible situations actually exists. The greater the initial array of possible situations, the greater the number of choices required to specify any particular situation. To the degree that we have some theoretical framework already available, the amount of information required to specify completely a given system is reduced. For example, assuming that the MacArthur distribution is valid, if we know the total number of species and the total number of individuals in the sample or the community, we already know the relative number of individuals in each species. The only questions that remain to be asked in reference to the distribution of numbers and species are "What is the rank order of the S species in the community?" and "What is the abundance of some species of known rank?" Once these have been determined, the abundance of each species has also been determined. The MacArthur distribution itself embodies a large amount of information, considerably reducing the conceivable alternatives in any natural community and correspondingly reducing the information required from a particular investigation in specifying the state of a particular community.

Let us assume a collection of empirically valid ecological generalizations. These generalizations can now be ranked as to their predictive power, if we define this power as their ability to increase our a priori information about any uninvestigated community at the expense of the new information yet to be acquired from that community. For example, if we know that two species always occur in association with one another, and in equal numbers, an enumeration of one permits us to make an a priori statement about the number of the other species present and correspondingly restricts the possible states of a community that has either of the species present. In this sense, we have already developed several rather powerful ecological laws, and it seems of interest at this stage to see how much predictability they give us and what types of laws may be envisioned for future development.

Most of the more powerful laws relate to how members of a community will interact and to the rates of these interactions, rather than to the spatial distribution and number of individuals. One of the simplest and most powerful generalizations is that, for any set of species constituting a community, the consumption of potential energy per unit time will be greater for populations that feed on plants than for populations that feed on other animals. This permits us, once we know the diet of a group of animals, to make fair predictions of their total abundance. It is also a fairly safe generality that the longest food chain that can be constructed in a community will have no more than five or conceivably six levels or links at the utmost.

The first of these laws is a very simple consequence of elementary physics and the conservation of energy. The second is not; rather, it is, at the moment, an empirical generalization from field observation. It can be made intuitively comprehensible in terms of the type of argument given earlier that would indicate that the total volume of the ecological world required to maintain a predator of a trophic level higher than 20 would exceed the area available on some of the continents. There is some indication that small islands, and other isolated pieces of the earth's surface, do not have sufficient area to maintain even the five or possibly six trophic levels that are observed under some circumstances. It is possible to conceive of predators that are small enough and ferocious enough to attempt to live off the top of a trophic pyramid, and thereby become a seventh, or even an eighth, trophic level. It is by no means clear why this situation has not occurred.

The answer to this and related questions must lie in the area of natural selection of communities as a whole, rather than being explained on the basis of natural selection operating on single species within communities. Consider, for example, the simple situation of a species N_1 consumed by a predator N_2. Making the simplest possible assumption, consider that $dN_1/dt = r_1 N_1 - aN_1 N_2$. If we consider the system N_1, N_2 to be in equilibrium, then $dN_1/dt = 0$. N_2 is proportional to the ratio r_1/a, but a is also proportional to the energy income of species N_2, since it is a measure of N_2's success in catching N_1. To the degree that population N_1 is actually controlled by predation, evolution will tend to maximize r_1; and this, as can be seen from our discussion of efficiency, is equivalent to maximizing the food-chain efficiency of the system N_1, N_2.

It is concurrently the case that the evolution of N_2 will be such as to maximize a, and should this process be very successful, species N_1 is likely to be eliminated because of excessive predation. N_2 must then either have alternate food or must itself become extinct. Clearly the alternate food cannot be on a higher trophic level than species N_2 itself, although it may be on a lower trophic level than species N_1.

The same arguments would apply in considering entire trophic levels. Here, excessively successful predation by trophic level n on trophic level $n - 1$ may eventually necessitate trophic level n switching its feeding to trophic level $n - 2$ (Hutchinson, 1959). This process tends to shorten the food chain, at the same time tending to maximize efficiencies.

These same simple equations also give some insight into the evolution of ecological diversity within a single trophic level. In a species limited by predation, there is continual selective pressure to escape from the predator—that is, to minimize a. There is counter-selection on the predator to succeed in its hunting process—that is, to maximize a. If there are two prey species, and they both evolve the same mechanism for escaping from their predator, the predator can evolve to counteract this escape mechanism and no advantage accrues to either prey species. If, however, two prey species become different from each other in their procedure of hiding or escaping from the predator, the predator must develop considerable behavioral complexity in order to keep the percentage of successful encounters with both prey as high as it had been previously. We have already noted that, where two species are coexistent in some ecological situation and are limited by predation, the stability of the system is increased by ecological diversification of the species, in the sense that the absence of diversity implies elimination of one of the species.

In general, then, we see that there is an evolutionary tendency to diversity, high efficiency, and food chains of limited length. But if there has been this tendency for diversity throughout the history of evolution, why is diversity as limited as it is? Two facts are available that seem to bear on this point. The first is the very simple generalization that the amount of physical space required for the maintenance of an organism is roughly proportional to the organism's size. The second is considerably less obvious at first glance. In order to meet stability conditions, two coexistent species in any environment must differ from each other ecologically to some significant degree. The point to determine is what percentage of the volume of the niche hyperspaces of two ecologically similar species constitutes the minimum percentage of nonoverlap that will permit continued coexistence of the species. Although absolute measurement of this value is impossible, some indication may be gained by anatomical comparison between pairs of species.

Hutchinson (1959) finds for a variety of birds and mammals that the trophic structures as represented by the skulls and beaks show relatively constant proportional differences between sympatric populations of very closely related pairs of species. The ratio of the size of the smaller to that of the larger species is $1:1\frac{1}{4}$. In general, then, we can conclude that there are a relatively large number of species of small animals and a smaller number of species of large animals. The size distribution of animals is regulated by trophic level considerations and by the general mosaic pattern of the environment (*cf.* Hairston, 1959, and Hutchinson, 1959). The total number of species available within each size category and ecological role is limited by the requirements that the ecological hyperspace of the various species cannot overlap excessively. Unfortunately, no precise formalization of these concepts is yet available.

The future development of theoretical community ecology will probably be based on considerations of community stability. It is known that any ecological change in a stable community will shift the entire community to a new stable state, although the theory of these stable states has not yet been formulated. The newer forms of mathematics, advanced probability theory, information theory, and so forth will all be utilized to develop models of communities. Thus far these models have not been particularly successful in making predictions that could not have otherwise been made; however, as further experimental work and field studies begin to delineate the properties that these models must have and set limiting and boundary conditions for their formulation, greater predictive success may be anticipated. We may, for example, conjecture that generalizations of the following sort will prove valid:

(1) Food-chain efficiencies and ecological efficiencies in nature are approximately constant for all species.

(2) Species-abundance distributions follow some modification of MacArthur's theoretical prediction.

(3) Population stability has some relatively simple relation to the physiological properties of the particular species.

(4) Community stability is in some sense proportional to food-web complexity.

And perhaps

(5) There exists a minimum anatomical diversity between sympatric species that will just permit their coexistence in nature.

Any such list of valid generalizations will set narrow limits to the properties of acceptable ecological theories. Any ecological theory that pretends to predictive power must in particular conform to these restrictions. The greater the number and precision of such generalizations, the less likely that ecological theory will wander into mere verbiage, unbridled speculations, and misleading metaphors. We may reasonably expect to have eventually a complete theory of ecology that will not only provide a guide for the practical solution of land utilization, pest eradication, and exploitation problems but will also permit us to start with an initial set of conditions on the earth's surface (derived from geological data) and construct a model that will incorporate genetics and ecology in such a way as to explain the past and also predict the future of evolution on earth.

Bibliography

ALLEE, W. C., 1951. *Cooperation among animals, with human implications,* New York: Schuman. 233 pages.

ANDREWARTHA, H. G., and BIRCH, L. C., 1954. *The distribution and abundance of animals,* Chicago: University of Chicago Press. xv + 782 pages.

ARMSTRONG, J. T., 1960. *The dynamics of* Daphnia pulex *populations and of* Dugesia tigrina *populations as modified by immigration,* Ph.D. dissertation, Department of Zoology, University of Michigan, Ann Arbor. 102 pages.

BARY, B. M., 1954. "Sea-water discoloration by living organisms," *New Zeal. Jour. Sci. and Technol.,* Ser. B, **34** (5) : 393–407.

———, and STUCKEY, R. G., 1950. "An occurrence in Wellington Harbour of *Cyclotrichium meunieri* Powers, a ciliate causing red water, with some additions to its morphology," *Roy. Soc. New Zeal. Trans. and Proc.,* **78:** 86–92.

BEAUCHAMP, R. S. A., and ULLYOTT, P., 1932. "Competitive relationships between certain species of fresh-water triclads," *Jour. Ecol.,* **20:** 200–208.

BEVERTON, J. H., and HOLT, S. J., 1958. *On the dynamics of exploited fish populations,* London: Fishery Investigations, Ser. II, Vol. XIX, Her Majesty's Stationery Office. 533 pages.

BIRCH, L. C., 1948. "The intrinsic rate of natural increase of an insect population," *Jour. Anim. Ecol.,* **17:** 15–26.

BODENHEIMER, F. S., 1938. *Problems of animal ecology,* London: Oxford University Press. vi + 183 pages.

———, 1958. *Animal ecology today.* Monographiae Biologicae, Vol. VI, Den Haag: Uitgeverij Dr. W. Junk. 276 pages.

BROOKS, J. L., 1946. "Cyclormorphosis in *Daphnia,*" *Ecol. Monog.,* **16:** 409–477.

BROWN, H. S., 1954. *The challenge of man's future: an inquiry concerning the condition of man during the years that lie ahead,* New York: Viking Press. 290 pages.

173

Burrell, H. J., 1927. *The platypus, its discovery, zoological position, form and characteristics, habits, life history, etc.*, Sydney: Angus & Robertson Ltd. 227 pages.

Cain, S. A., and Evans, F. C., 1952. "The distribution patterns of three plant species in an old-field community in southeastern Michigan," *Contr. Lab. Vert. Biol. Univ. Mich.*, **52:** 1–11.

Calhoun, John B., 1952. "The social aspects of population dynamics," *Jour. Mammal.*, **33**(2): 139–159.

Chew, F., 1953. "Results of hydrographic and chemical investigations in the region of the 'red tide' bloom on the west coast of Florida in November 1952," *Bul. Mar. Sci. Gulf and Caribbean*, **2**(4): 610–625.

Christian, J. J., 1956. "Adrenal and reproductive responses to population size in mice from freely growing populations," *Ecol.*, **37**(2): 258–273.

Clements, F. E., and Shelford, V. E., 1939. *Bio-ecology*, New York: John Wiley & Sons. vi + 425 pages.

Cole, L. C., 1954a. "The population consequences of life history phenomena," *Quart. Rev. Biol.*, **29:** 103–137.

———, 1954b. "Some features of random cycles," *Jour. Wildlife Mangt.*, **18:** 107–109.

D'Ancona, Umberto, 1954. *The struggle for existence*, Leiden: E. J. Brill. xi + 274 pages.

Darling, F. F., 1955. *West Highland survey*, London: Oxford University Press. viii + 438 pages.

Deevey, Edward S., 1947. "Life tables for natural populations of animals," *Quart. Rev. Biol.*, **22**(4): 283–314.

Dice, L. R., 1952. *Natural communities*, Ann Arbor: University of Michigan Press. x + 547 pages.

Dublin, L. L., Lotka, A. J., and Spiegelman, M., 1949. *Length of life: a study of the life table*, rev. ed., New York: Ronald Press. xxv + 379 pages.

Edmondson, W. T., 1944. "Ecological studies of sessile Rotatoria. Part I. Factors affecting distribution," *Ecol. Monog.*, **14:** 31–36.

Elton, C. S., 1958. *The ecology of invasions by animals and plants*, London: Methuen & Company. 181 pages.

Engelmann, M., 1960. *The role of the arthropods in the soil of an old field*, Ph.D. dissertation, Department of Zoology, University of Michigan, Ann Arbor. 81 pages.

Errington, P. L., 1946. "Predation and vertebrate populations," *Quart. Rev. Biol.*, **21**: 145–177, 221–245.

Evans, F. C., and Cain, Stanley A., 1952. "Preliminary studies on the vegetation of an old-field community in southeastern Michigan," *Contr. Lab. Vert. Biol. Univ. Mich.*, **51**: 1–17.

———, and Dahl, E., 1955. "The vegetational structure of an abandoned field in southeastern Michigan and its relation to environmental factors," *Ecol.*, **36**(4): 685–706.

Fisher, R. A., 1958. *The genetical theory of natural selection*, New York: Dover Publications. xiv +291 pages. (Oxford: Clarendon Press, 1930, x + 272 pages.)

———, Corbet, A. Steven, and Williams, C. B., 1943. "The relation between the number of species and the number of individuals in a random sample of an animal population," *Jour. Anim. Ecol.*, **12**(1): 42–58.

Flower, S. S., 1938. "Further notes on the duration of life in animals. IV. Birds," *Proc. Zool. Soc. Lond.*, **108**(A): 195–235.

———, 1944. "Persistent growth in the tortoise, *Testudo graeca*, for thirty-nine years, with other notes concerning that species," *Proc. Zool. Soc. Lond.*, **114**: 451–455.

———, 1947. "Further notes on the duration of life in mammals. V. The alleged and actual ages to which elephants live," *Proc. Zool. Soc. Lond.*, **117**: 680–688.

Frank, P. W., 1957. "Coaction in laboratory populations of two species of *Daphnia*," *Ecol.*, **38**(3): 510–519.

———, 1960. "Prediction of population growth form in *Daphnia pulex* cultures," *Amer. Nat.*, **94** (878): 357–372.

———, Boll, C. D., and Kelly, R. W., 1957. "Vital statistics of laboratory cultures of *Daphnia pulex* De Geer as related to density," *Physiol. Zool.*, **30**: 287–305.

Gause, G. F., 1934. *The struggle for existence*, Baltimore: Williams & Wilkins. vii + 163 pages.

———, 1935. *La théorie mathématique de la lutte pour la vie*. Paris: Hermann et Cie. 61 pages.

Hairston, N. G., 1959. "Species abundance and community organization," *Ecol.*, **40**(3): 404–416.

———, and Byers, George W., 1954. "The soil arthropods of a field in southern Michigan: a study in community ecology," *Contr. Lab. Vert. Biol. Univ. Mich.*, **64**: 1–37.

Hediger, H., 1950. *Wild animals in captivity*, London: Butterworths Scientific Publications. ix + 207 pages.

Huffaker, C. B., 1958. "Experimental studies on predation: dispersion factors and predator-prey oscillations," *Hilgardia,* **27:** 343–383.

――――, and Kennett, C. E., 1956. "Experimental studies on predation: predation and cyclamen-mite populations on strawberries in California," *Hilgardia,* **26**(4): 191–222.

Hutchinson, G. E., 1947. "A note on the theory of competition between two social species," *Ecol.,* **28:** 319–321.

――――, 1948. "Circular causal systems in ecology," *Annals N. Y. Acad. Sci.,* **50,** Art. 4: 221–246.

――――, 1950. "The biogeochemistry of vertebrate excretion," *Bul. Amer. Mus. Natl. Hist.,* **96:** 1–554.

――――, 1951. "Copepodology for the ornithologist," *Ecol.,* **32**(3): 571–577.

――――, 1953. "The concept of pattern in ecology," *Proc. Acad. Nat. Sci.,* Philadelphia, **105:** 1–12.

――――, 1954. "Notes on oscillatory populations," *Jour. Wildlife Mangt.,* **18**(1): 107–109.

――――, 1957. "Concluding remarks," *Cold Spring Harbor Symposia on Quantitative Biology,* **22:** 415–427.

――――, 1959. "Homage to Santa Rosalia or Why are there so many kinds of animals," *Amer. Nat.,* **93**(870): 145–159.

――――, and Ripley, D. E., 1954. "Gene dispersal and the ethology of the Rhinocerotidae," *Evolution,* **8**(2): 178–179.

Hutner, S. H., Provasoli, L., McLaughlin, J. A., and Pintner, I. J., 1956. "Biochemical geography: some aspects of recent vitamin research," *Geog. Rev.,* **46**(3): 404–407.

Kac, M., 1954. Appendix to Cole, 1954b. (See above.)

Kennedy, J. S., 1937. "The humidity reactions of the African migratory locust *Locusta migratoria migratorioides* R. and F. gregarious phase," *Jour. Expt. Biol.,* **14:** 187–197.

Kierstead, H., and Slobodkin, L. B., 1953. "The size of water masses containing plankton blooms," *Sears Found. Jour. Mar. Res.,* **12**(1): 141–147.

King, J. A., 1955. "Social behavior, social organization, and population dynamics in a black-tailed prairie dog town in the Black Hills of South Dakota," *Contr. Lab. Vert. Biol. Univ. Mich.,* **67:** 123.

Kohn, Alan J., 1959. "The ecology of Conus in Hawaii," *Ecol. Monog.,* **29**(1): 47–90.

Kostitsyn, V. A., 1937. *Biologie mathématique,* Paris: Librairie Armand Colin. 223 pages.

KURTEN, B., 1959. "Rates of evolution in fossil mammals," *Cold Spring Harbor Symposia on Quantitative Biology*, **24:** 205–215.

LACK, D. L., 1947. *Darwin's finches*, Cambridge, England: Cambridge University Press. x + 208 pages.

———, 1954. *The natural regulation of animal numbers*, Oxford: Clarendon Press. viii + 343 pages.

LESLIE, P. H., and PARK, T., 1949. "The intrinsic rate of natural increase of *Tribolium castaneum* Herbst," *Ecol.*, **30:** 469–477.

LINDEMAN, RAYMOND L., 1942. "The trophic-dynamic aspect of ecology," *Ecol.*, **23**(4): 399–418.

LOTKA, A. J., 1931. "The structure of a growing population," *Human Biol.*, **3:** 459–493.

———, 1934. "Théorie analytique des associations biologiques," *Actualités Scientifiques et Industrielles*, **187:** 1–45.

———, 1956. *Elements of mathematical biology*, New York: Dover Publications. xxx + 460 pages. (Baltimore: Williams & Wilkins, 1925. x + 460 pages.)

MACARTHUR, ROBERT, 1955. "Fluctuations of animal populations, and a measure of community stability," *Ecol.*, **36**(3): 533–536.

———, 1957. "On the relative abundance of bird species," *Proc. Nat. Acad. Sci. U. S.*, **43:** 293–295.

———, 1958. "Population ecology of some warblers of northern coniferous forests," *Ecol.*, **39**(4): 599–619.

MACFADYEN, A., 1957. *Animal ecology, aims and methods*, London: Sir Isaac Pitman and Sons, Ltd. 255 pages.

McLAREN, I. A., 1958. "The biology of the ringed seal, *Phoco Hispida* Schreber, in the eastern Canadian Arctic," *Bul. Fish. Res. Bo. Canada*, **118:** 1–97.

MALTHUS, T. B., 1798. *First essay on population* (reprinted 1926), London: Macmillan & Co., Ltd. ix + 396 pages.

MARGALEF, D. RAMON, 1958. "Information theory in ecology," *Gen. Systems*, **3:** 36–71. (Trans. from *Memorias de la Real Academia de Ciencias y Artes de Barcelona*, **23:** 373–449, Nov., 1957.)

MERRIMAN, D., 1941. "Studies on the striped bass (*Roccus saxatilis*) of the Atlantic coast," *Fish. Bul. U. S. Fish and Wildlife Service*, **50:** ii + 77 pages.

MURIE, A., 1944. "The wolves of Mt. McKinley," U. S. Dept. Interior, Nat'l. Park Serv.; *Fauna of the Nat'l. Parks of the U. S.*, Fauna Ser. **5:** xix + 238 pages.

MURPHY, R. L., 1923. "The oceanography of the Peruvian littoral with reference to the abundance and distribution of marine life," *Geogr. Rev.*, **13:** 64–85.

Neyman, J., Park, T., and Scott, E. L., 1958. "Struggle for existence; the Tribolium model: biological and statistical aspects," *Gen. Systems,* **3:** 152–179.

Nicholson, A. J., 1954. "Compensatory reactions of populations to stresses, and their evolutionary significance," *Austral. Jour. Zool.,* **2**(1): 1–8.

———, 1957. "The self-adjustment of populations to change," *Cold Spring Harbor Symposia on Quantitative Biology,* **22:** 153–173.

Norris, M. J., 1954. "Sexual maturation in the desert locust," *Anti-Locust Bul.,* **18:** 1–44.

Organ, J., 1961. "Studies of the local distribution, life history, and population dynamics of the salamander genus *Desmognathus* in Virginia," *Ecol. Monog.,* **31**(2): (in press).

Osborn, F., 1948. *Our plundered planet,* Boston: Little, Brown. xiv + 217 pages.

Park, T., 1955. "Experimental competition in beetles, with some general implications," in J. B. Cragg and N. W. Pirie, *The numbers of man and animals,* London: Oliver and Boyd. 152 pages.

Patten, Bernard C., 1959. "An introduction to the cybernetics of the ecosystem trophic-dynamic aspect," *Ecol.,* **40**(2): 221–231.

Paynter, R. A., 1947. "The fate of banded Kent Island herring gulls," *Bird-Banding,* **28**(4): 156–170.

Pearl, R., 1928. "Experiments on longevity," *Quart. Rev. Biol.,* **3:** 391–407.

Pitelka, F. A., 1957. "Some aspects of population structure in the short-term cycle of the brown lemming in northern Alaska," *Cold Spring Harbor Symposia on Quantitative Biology,* **22:** 237–251.

Pratt, D. M., 1943. "Analysis of population development in *Daphnia* at different temperatures," *Biol. Bul.,* **85:** 116–140.

Preston, F. W., 1948. "The commonness, and rarity, of species," *Ecol.,* **29:** 254–283.

Rainey, R. C., 1951. "Weather and the movements of locust swarms: a new hypothesis," *Nature,* **168:** 1057–1060.

Richman, Sumner, 1958. "The transformation of energy by *Daphnia pulex,*" *Ecol. Monog.,* **28:** 273–291.

Ricker, W. E., 1954. "Effects of compensatory mortality upon population abundance," *Jour. Wildlife Mangt.,* **18**(1): 45–51.

RICKER, W. E., 1958. "Handbook of computations for biological statistics of fish populations," *Bull. Fish. Res. Bo. Canada,* **119**: 1–300.

RIPLEY, S. D., 1952. "Territorial and sexual behavior in the great Indian rhinoceros, a speculation," *Ecol.,* **33**: 570–573.

SEARS, P. B., 1935. *Deserts on the march,* Norman: University of Oklahoma Press. 231 pages.

SKELLAM, J. G., 1957. "Comment on paper of L. C. Birch," *Cold Spring Harbor Symposia on Quantitative Biology,* **22**: 217.

SLOBODKIN, L. B., 1953a. "On social single species populations," *Ecol.,* **34**(2): 430–434.

————, 1953b. "A possible initial condition for red tides on the coast of Florida," *Sears Found. Jour. Mar. Res.,* **12**(1): 148–155.

————, 1954a. "Population dynamics in *Daphnia obtusa* Kurz," *Ecol. Monog.,* **24**: 69–88.

————, 1954b. "Cycles in animal populations," *Amer. Sci.,* **42** (4): 658–660, 666.

————, 1959. "Energetics in *Daphnia pulex* populations," *Ecol.,* **40**(2): 232–243.

————, 1960. "Ecological energy relationships at the population level," *Amer. Nat.,* **94**(876): 213–236.

————, 1961. "Preliminary ideas for a predictive theory of ecology," *Amer. Nat.,* **95**(3): 147–153.

————, and RICHMAN, S., 1956. "The effect of removal of fixed percentages of the new born on size and variability in populations of *Daphnia pulicaria* (Forbes)," *Limnology and Oceanography,* **1**(3): 209–237.

SMITH, FREDERICK E., 1952. "Experimental methods in population dynamics: a critique," *Ecol.,* **33**(4): 441–450.

————, 1954. "Quantitative aspects of population growth," in *Dynamics of growth processes,* E. Boell, ed., Princeton, N. J.: Princeton University Press. 304 pages.

————, and BAYLOR, E. R., 1953. "Color responses in the cladocera and their ecological significance," *Amer. Nat.,* **87**: 49–55.

SOUTHWICK, C. H., 1955. "Regulatory mechanisms of house-mouse populations: social behavior affecting litter survival," *Ecol.,* **36**(4): 627–634.

STANLEY, J., 1949. "A mathematical theory of the growth of populations of the flour beetle, *Tribolium confusum* Duv. VII. A study of the 'retunneling' problem," *Ecol.,* **30**: 209–222.

STRECKER, R. L., 1954. "Regulatory mechanisms in house-mouse populations: the effect of limited food supply on an unconfined population," *Ecol.,* **35**(2): 249–253.

STRECKER, R. L., and EMLEN, J. T., JR., 1953. "Regulatory mechanisms in house-mouse populations: the effect of limited food supply on a confined population," *Ecol.,* **34**(2): 375–385.

SWAMMERDAM, J., 1681. *Ephemeri vita, or the natural history and anatomy of the ephemeron, a fly that lives but five hours,* London: H. Faithorne and J. Kersey. 44 pages.

TEAL, J. M., 1957. "Community metabolism in a temperate cold spring," *Ecol. Monog.,* **23**: 41–78.

THOMAS, W. L. (ed.), 1956. *International symposium on man's role in changing the face of the earth,* Chicago: University of Chicago Press. xxxviii + 1193 pages.

THOMPSON, SIR D. W., 1940. *Science and the classics,* London: Oxford University Press, H. Milford. viii + 264 pages.

———, 1943. *On growth and form,* New York: Macmillan. 1116 pages.

THOMPSON, W. R., with H. E. SOPER, 1931. "On the reproduction of organisms with overlapping generations," *Bul. Ent. Res.,* **22**: 139–152.

ULRICH, H., 1940. "Uber den Generationswechsel und seine Bedingungen," *Naturwiss.,* **28**: 569–576, 586–591.

UTIDA, S., 1953. "Interspecific competition between two species of bean weevil," *Ecol.,* **34**(2): 301–307.

———, 1957. "Population fluctuation, an experimental and theoretical approach," *Cold Spring Harbor Symposia on Quantitative Biology,* **22**: 139–151.

VERNADSKY, W. I., 1944. "Problems of biogeochemistry. II. The fundamental matter-energy difference between the living and the inert natural bodies of the biosphere," *Trans. Conn. Acad. Arts and Sci.,* **35**: 483–517.

VOGT, W., 1948. *Road to survival,* New York: William Sloane. xvi + 335 pages.

WILLIAMS, W. T., and LAMBERT, J. M., 1959. "Multivariate methods in plant ecology. I. Association analysis in plant communities," *Ecol.,* **47**(1): 83–101.

WOLFENDEN, H. H., 1954. *Population statistics and their compilation,* Chicago: University of Chicago Press. 258 pages.

WOODRUFF, L. L., 1912. "Observations on the origin and sequence of the protozoan fauna of hay infusions," *Jour. Exper. Zool.,* **12**: 205–264.

index

181